LIFE NATURE LIBRARY

THE LAND AND WILDLIFE OF
AFRICA

LIFE NATURE LIBRARY

THE LAND AND WILDLIFE OF
AFRICA

by Archie Carr
and The Editors of LIFE

TIME INCORPORATED
NEW YORK

About the Author

Archie Carr first visited Africa in 1952 as a member of a team studying malaria, bilharziasis and filariasis in Nyasaland. Being a biologist whose sense of curiosity is so highly developed as to be almost wayward, he began soaking up information about pythons, fly spouts, lions and fishes as fast as he did about mosquitoes. Everything about the continent obsessed him. He went back in 1955, 1956 and 1963 to study turtle migrations, doubling on the last as a delegate to the meetings of the International Union for the Conservation of Nature, held in Nairobi. From these visits, from the catholicity of his interests and from the extensive studies that they have stimulated, Dr. Carr has become widely informed about African ecology and is understandably concerned about it. "The most stirring thing I learned about Africa," he wrote recently, "was how fast its classic landscapes are being lost." This is Dr. Carr's second book on Africa; the first, *Ulendo*, was published in 1964. He is also the author of *The Reptiles*, an earlier volume in the LIFE Nature Library.

ON THE COVER: Two giraffes are silhouetted against an East African sunset. Giraffes prefer dry savanna country where the ground is hard and can support their great weight —up to two tons—without their relatively small hoofs sinking in.

Contents

TIME-LIFE BOOKS

EDITOR
Maitland A. Edey
EXECUTIVE EDITOR
Jerry Korn
TEXT DIRECTOR   ART DIRECTOR
Martin Mann   Sheldon Cotler
CHIEF OF RESEARCH
Beatrice T. Dobie
PICTURE EDITOR
Robert G. Mason
Assistant Text Directors:
Harold C. Field, Ogden Tanner
Assistant Art Director: Arnold C. Holeywell
Assistant Chief of Research: Martha Turner
•

PUBLISHER
Rhett Austell
General Manager: Joseph C. Hazen Jr.
Circulation Director: Joan D. Manley
Marketing Director: Carter Smith
Business Manager: John D. McSweeney
Publishing Board: Nicholas Benton, Louis Bronzo,
James Wendell Forbes

LIFE MAGAZINE

EDITOR: Edward K. Thompson
MANAGING EDITOR: George P. Hunt
PUBLISHER: Jerome S. Hardy

LIFE NATURE LIBRARY

EDITOR: Maitland A. Edey
Associate Editor: Percy Knauth
Assistants to the Editor: Robert Morton, John Paul Porter
Designer: Paul Jensen
Staff Writers: Dale Brown, Timothy Carr,
Mary Louise Grossman, Peter Wood
Chief Researcher: Martha Turner
Researchers: David Bridge, Doris Bry, Peggy Bushong,
Joan Chasin, Jacqueline Coates, Nancy Jacobsen,
Paula Norworth, Carol Phillippe, Marjorie Pickens,
Susan Rayfield, Carollee Rosenblatt, Roxanna Sayre,
Nancy Shuker, Iris Unger, John von Hartz

EDITORIAL PRODUCTION
Color Director: Robert L. Young
Copy Staff: Marian Gordon Goldman, Joan Chambers,
Dolores A. Littles
Picture Bureau: Margaret K. Goldsmith, Joan T. Lynch
Art Assistants: James D. Smith, Mark A. Binn,
John Newcomb

The text for this book was written by Archie Carr, the picture essays by the editorial staff. The following members and departments of Time Inc. helped to produce the book: LIFE staff photographers Alfred Eisenstaedt, Eliot Elisofon, Fritz Goro, Dmitri Kessel and George Silk; the Chief of the LIFE Picture Library, Doris O'Neil; the Chief of the TIME-LIFE News Service, Richard M. Clurman; the Chief of the Time Inc. Bureau of Editorial Reference, Peter Draz.

Introduction

SOMETHING new is certainly coming out of Africa these days, something just as dramatic as the appearance of unknown species like the okapi in 1900 and the African peacock in 1937. We are discovering patterns in the fabric of life in which the habits and life histories of individual species of plants and animals are the threads. It is moderately easy to watch the larger animals, to find how they use their environment, how they differ from each other in their demands upon it and how they contribute to the maintenance of their chosen habitat, although little of this work has been done yet. It is altogether harder to find out how the insect fauna of any habitat is doing the same thing, how it is contributing to the efficiency of the turnover of matter and energy.

I can think of no book on Africa which brings to one's notice this complexity and interwoven quality so effectively as Archie Carr's present volume. Many of us who have worked in Africa have been interested primarily in the larger animals or the birds, or in forestry or botany. In our preoccupation with these we may not have stopped and stared long enough at less obvious relationships. Archie Carr is a zoologist with a wide knowledge of the tropics, so when he got into Africa he saw the natural scene of rain forest, mountain, plain and marsh in a more all-round way, and from this we now benefit in this delightful book.

We have grown to understand that conservation of the wildlife of Africa depends largely on preservation of the several habitats in which it lives. Our growing awareness that communities of plants and animals develop into ecosystems as complex as the environmental conditions will allow has led us to realize that to remove species from an ecosystem is to make it less efficient as an energy-circulating and energy-conserving system. In countless places in Africa the incoming European has thought that where there are so many hoofed animals must surely be a good place for stock raising. But instead of substituting 20 or 30 species of domesticated animals for those removed, he has put one or two, or at most three—cattle, sheep and goats—and has found that productivity is nothing like as good. Looking at a tropical forest, he has said some of the "weed trees" should be removed and more of the desirable timber-producing species planted; but the tropical rain forest, the most elaborate of all plant communities in the world, does not work like that. Each species has its place and niche, and so tender is this complex ecosystem that any considerable interference prevents its regeneration. The great trees go and also the creatures which live up in the canopy and under the surface of the soil. The very soil itself disappears if it is not shaded.

This understanding is the new thing coming out of Africa, now and for a long time to come.

F. FRASER DARLING
Vice President
The Conservation Foundation

WHERE REAL IMPALAS ONCE MADE THEIR HIGH-FLYING LEAPS, BRONZE IMPALAS, THE WORK OF THE SOUTH AFRICAN SCULPTOR HERMANN WALD,

1 The Dark Continent

NOW FORM PART OF A FOUNTAIN IN A PARK IN THE CENTER OF JOHANNESBURG. TO WALD, IMPALAS ARE "THE BALLERINAS OF THE GAME PRESERVE"

W<small>HEN</small> most people think of African animals it is probably the lion that comes first to mind. Being strong, huge and able to roar, the lion stands out as the zoological spirit of the place. But despite his many imposing traits, the lion is, zoogeographically speaking, pretty small potatoes.

I don't mean to depreciate the animal. The lion is splendid, really. At least the lioness is. They say it is mainly lionesses that get things done. But to a zoogeographer *Leo leo* is simply a cat, and cats are found all about the earth. In the not-too-distant past, there were cats bigger than any lion ever was, and they were fancier too. So, as stirring as lions are, they are fundamentally a very widespread phenomenon, and a chapter on the really distinctive features of the African fauna ought not dwell too long on lions. It ought to focus on some of the true zoogeographic marvels, like the aardvark and the naked mole rat.

First, however, one ought to take a quick look at the lay of the land itself. The continent of Africa is essentially a giant plateau. Except for occasional flooding of its edges it has been extraordinarily stable since Precambrian times. For some 60 million years the only mountain folding was that which made the Atlas Mountains in the extreme north. These are really an extension of the European Alps and are geologically more European than African.

But if mountain folding has been slight, volcanic activity has occurred intermittently from the earliest recorded geologic times right down to the present. Most of the highest mountains are old volcanoes. Mount Kilimanjaro, snow-capped and, at 19,340 feet, the highest peak in Africa, is a volcano. So are many of the other principal peaks, like Mount Kenya, Mount Meru, Mount Elgon in East Africa and Cameroon Mountain in West Africa. The Ruwenzori range—the famous Mountains of the Moon—is not volcanic.

VOLCANISM continues even today in East Africa and the Cameroons. There was a major eruption in the eastern Congo between 1938 and 1942, and another smaller one in the Cameroons in 1959. Besides its effects on major topography, volcanic activity may have been involved in other ways in the look of the fauna and flora of Africa. According to new views the early history of humanity in East Africa may have been tied in with volcanism. It could have been a source of fires that helped spread the type of savanna landscape in which much of human evolution may have occurred. It could possibly have been also a source of fire used as one of the earliest of human tools. It may have been important as an agency that dammed streams and made lakes with shores that were a propitious environment for the humanization of the aimless old ape men. It possibly even provided trace elements that may have been responsible for spurts of gigantism in many animal species. While all these ideas are conjectural, a great deal of talented effort is being spent on efforts to get to the bottom of them.

Much of Africa's volcanic activity has been concentrated along an immense 4,000-mile-long crack in the earth's surface, known as the Great Rift Valley. This is one of the most astonishing features on the earth's crust. It runs roughly north-south in eastern Africa, from Mozambique through Tanganyika (continental Tanzania), Kenya and the Ethiopian highlands into Asia Minor.

In Africa the rift is hundreds of feet deep—thousands in some places. It varies in width from 30 to 50 miles and contains most of Africa's great lakes: Albert, Edward, Rudolf, Kivu, Nyasa and Tanganyika. The bottom of Lake Tanganyika, the second-deepest lake in the world, is 2,200 feet below sea level; its surface is 2,500 feet above sea level. Lake Nyasa is 2,300 feet deep and, like Tanganyika, is narrow and troughlike, being 360 miles long and only 15 to 50 miles wide. The rift forks north of Lake Nyasa, and in the area between the two sections of the rift lies Lake Victoria, which, although much shallower than Nyasa and Tanganyika, is in area second only to Lake Superior among the fresh-water lakes of the world.

In spite of the geologic stability of the African land mass, the animals that now inhabit it have had very different zoogeographic histories. Their ancestors got into the place at different times, they came in from different origins, and since their arrival they have evolved at different rates. Some of the old stocks have been strongly changed by evolution, and some of the oldest of them have now died out everywhere except in Africa. The exclusively African forms are spoken of as endemics; one says of them that they are *endemic* to Africa.

As you see it on a map, Africa looks much like South America. Both are southern continents with the equator running across their midsections. Each is connected with the rest of the dry-land world only at its uppermost border; each is otherwise surrounded by ocean. Each has a wide range of topographic diversity, including snowcapped mountains and vast river systems. A closer zoological appraisal of the two, however, will show that South America has many more peculiar kinds of animals confined to it than Africa has.

The reason for this is that it has had a long history as an island continent. The disruptions of the connections of South America with the outside world have been prolonged and have come at critical times in the spread of modern groups of animals that otherwise might have moved in and brought intolerable competition to the older, home-grown types. Africa, by contrast, has remained in contact with the world to the north during the main times of dispersal of most vertebrate groups. It has been so stable that it is often lumped with Eurasia and North America as a single paleozoogeographic region.

The African fauna shows the effects of both isolation and repeated contacts with the outside world. One barrier to dispersal into and out of Africa has been the Mediterranean Sea, or rather a much larger, ancient geologic feature known as the Tethys Sea, of which the Mediterranean is just a vestige. Another barrier has been the deserts of the north. Today when a zoologist speaks of Africa, it is Africa south of the Sahara that usually is meant. Very little movement of animals takes place across the desert, and this is one of the factors that have molded the look of modern African wildlife. On the other hand, the Sahara has not always been a barrier. Pictures made by prehistoric man on desert rocks show animals that surely must have eaten the leaves and grass of a wetter country than that which surrounds those rocks today. Moreover, in the desert oases, there are several kinds of fresh-water fishes which could only have got there via streams long since vanished. The full story of the climate of the Sahara region has not been worked out in detail, but a growing mass of geologic, paleontologic and archeologic information shows that there have been corridors of greener, more livable land running through or around the desert at various times in the past and that some of these have existed quite recently.

OF all vertebrate animals, it is the fresh-water fishes which, by their presence, absence and relationships, tell the most about the past history of a land. As Philip Darlington says in his magnificent book *Zoogeography*, "If there is such a thing as a general pattern of animal distribution, the fresh-water fishes ought to show it perhaps better than any other animals, and they do in fact show broad patterns which are well defined and very informative." The reasons for this are obvious. Fishes of fresh water find dry land an almost insuperable barrier, and most of them are just as unable to put up with the salt water of the sea. Thus they can neither walk nor swim to new places, and their dispersal in most cases must depend upon making their way through stream systems.

This generalization is not wholly valid, but it is a pretty good one, and its application to African zoogeography is clear and striking. To the zoogeographer Africa is, above all, a land of fishes. Both as an asylum for fantastic old

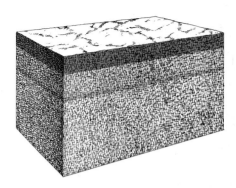

HOW RIFTS ARE FORMED

What is now the Great Rift Valley in Africa may have started as a peneplain —a land surface eroded nearly flat with various strata of sedimentary rock underneath (above). Below are shown the effects of deep crustal movements that tended to pull the earth's surface apart (white arrows) and allow larger blocks in between to sink down. This happened along parallel fault planes, the layers of rock sliding past one another and producing the steplike formations in the sidewalls of the rift. Meanwhile, long, deep, narrow lakes like Tanganyika and Nyasa formed in the bottom of the trough.

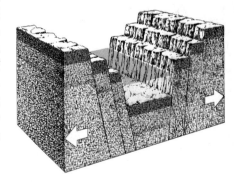

kinds that are no longer found anywhere else and as a stage for recent explosive fish evolution, no part of the world can match it.

The salient features of this engrossing fish fauna are: (a) archaic fishes; (b) fishes that are peculiarly and unevenly distributed; and (c) furiously evolving fishes. As one would expect, the first two categories, on close inspection, turn out to be more or less the same. The most ancient groups, obviously left over from times when Africa had land connections different from those now, should logically be the ones that show the greatest gaps in their present world distribution, and they are. The rapidly evolving fishes are mostly found in the East African lakes, and the majority of them belong to the family Cichlidae.

As for archaic fishes, nothing can quite match the famous marine coelacanth *Latimeria*, the living-fossil fish discovered in 1938 off East London, South Africa. There was great and appropriate fanfare over this find. The coelacanths are a line of fishes that arose 300 million years ago and have changed almost not at all since. Until *Latimeria* was found they were known only as fossils. They were animals you could get a look at only by splitting rocks—not by lowering a line into the ocean. Since the chance recovery of the first specimen several more have been caught in the Mozambique Channel and carefully studied. Since *Latimeria* had theretofore been believed to have been extinct for 70 million years, fishing it out of its lost world was an almost incredible occurrence. But actually, Africa has fishes almost this archaic in its inland waters. Two other groups in the fresh waters there have also maintained their antique architectural plans. These are the lungfishes and the bichirs. More will be said of these unbelievably durable creatures in the chapter that follows.

M ost of the reptiles and amphibians of Africa belong to worldwide or to Old World groups. There are, however, a few conspicuous cases of kinships with distant South America. The primitive clawed frogs are one of these, the iguanid lizards of Madagascar are another, and the side-necked turtles of the family Pelomedusidae are another. The most exclusively African groups are a family of frogs (Phrynomeridae) related to the narrow-mouthed toads, and two families of lizards—the girdle-tailed lizards, which are mainly South African, and the plated lizard, shared only with Madagascar. For the rest, the herpetological fauna is rich, but not particularly unusual. The array of colubrid snakes in Africa is tremendous, for instance, but this is a family found almost all over the world. More surprising are some of the gaps that exist. There are no salamanders or hylid tree frogs south of the Sahara, for example. There are no pit vipers anywhere on the continent.

From the standpoint of world zoogeography, Africa is not especially noteworthy for its bird fauna. This does not mean that there are not plenty of birds there. There are birds all over the place, and many of them are striking or of surpassingly colorful kinds. To anyone who knows the diversity of the African birds of prey or has seen the stunning congregations of waterfowl about some of the East African lakes, or a paradise whydah swooping between thorn trees, or a quarter of a million queleas in one dense cloud, or has watched a honey guide at work coaxing a honey badger along to a bee tree—to say to such a man that the bird fauna of Africa is undistinguished will sound to him wholly irresponsible. Some of the finest shows of birds in the world can be seen in Africa. But this particular chapter is, as I have already said, concerned with the most *distinctive* animals of Africa, and distinction of the kind in question does not come from beauty, size or abundance alone. It is achieved by lacking kinsmen in other places, by being an exclusive feature of the region one lives in. In this sense, African ornithology is not spectacular.

Some of the special oddities are the ostrich, the secretary bird, the hammerhead stork, the touracos, or plantain eaters, and the mousebirds. All of these belong to families which, according to current ornithological opinion, are restricted to Africa. Although a fairly familiar creature, the ostrich is probably the most set apart of the lot. Some ornithologists lump ostriches with the extinct elephant birds and moas, and with the living emus, rheas and other flightless birds in a special group, ratites. But these other earthbound birds have features that suggest that they may have separately evolved from one flying ancestor and the ostrich from another, and this qualifies it as the most distinctive of all the birds of the Ethiopian region. The range of the ostrich once extended widely into Asia. It was extirpated within historic times from Arabia and Syria. Today it ranges from the Atlas Mountains to the Cape of Good Hope.

The hammerhead is a relative of the storks, or at least it looks more like a stork than anything else. Its most arresting trait is the size of its nest, an enormous pile of sticks with an entrance in the side. Inside, the nest is lined with clay and has three chambers, the top one for the very young, a middle chamber for adolescent birds, and a third which is used as a vestibule and as a lookout room. The touracos are mostly about the size of a pigeon or small hen, with long tails and with an ability to run and scramble along the limbs of trees. They are really running birds, not of the open ground but of trees. They are very noisy, and many of them are among the most brilliantly colored birds in Africa. The mousebirds, an endemic African order, get their name from their mammalian look as they run about on limbs and trunks of trees. They have heavy hooked claws, their outer toes work either in the forward or backward position, and their feathers are loose and hairlike. The other most characteristic birds of the region are the river martin, six species of tree hoopoes, 42 species of bush shrikes, 13 species of helmet shrikes, three kinds of buffalo weavers, nine of widow birds, and two of tickbirds.

Although the list of endemic types is fairly meager, Africa has an overwhelming number of birds that also occur in Europe and Asia, some of them living there permanently, many others coming in during migration. The country of Kenya lists 622 species of birds found within its borders either as residents or transients. Kenya is almost the same size as the Canadian province of Alberta, which claims only 317 birds. In fact all of North America north of Mexico contains only 775 known species. For the entire African continent the figure may run as high as 2,500.

THE mammals of Africa are many and varied. The most arresting aspect of the mammal fauna is the association of big ungulates and carnivores found on the veld, although some of the smaller, humbler creatures are more the true essence of the land. Like the other groups of vertebrates, the mammals show strong affinities with those of Asia. If you come upon a pangolin in the forest, for instance, you would no doubt conclude that this curious scaly anteater could exist nowhere but right there in Africa; but you would be wrong. Pangolins also live in Asia.

Speaking of anteaters, there is another kind of medium-sized ant-eating animal that not only looks offbeat but is actually as completely African as any mammal could easily be. This is the aardvark. The name means earth pig in Afrikaans, but the animal has nothing to do with the pigs, and except for the tip of its snout, does not look as much like one as its name would indicate. The aardvark is found from Senegal and the Sudan to the Cape of Good Hope, in almost any open country in which there are great numbers of ants or termites in the earth. It is a stockily built animal, from four to six feet long, with scant hair, big jackasslike ears and a long tubular snout tipped with a flat disk perforated by the nostrils. It has short, heavy legs for digging, a short pointed tail and has been set apart in a special order not shared with any other animal.

Despite its size and relative abundance, the aardvark, being nocturnal and confirmedly subterranean, is seldom seen. I have never seen one. I regret this. I have peered down aardvark burrows and have listened vainly at the mouths of them for any small sound of the glamorous animal. I once had my teeth jarred when the car I was riding in ran suddenly over a patch of holes aardvarks had made. The ranger said they had been overturning the clay of the road to get at something or other. I even once suggested to fellow travelers that we all set to with shovels and round out our acquaintance with the savanna fauna by digging an aardvark out of his hole, but nothing came of this.

OF insectivores, relatives of the moles, shrews and hedgehogs, there are only three wholly African-mainland families. These are the jumping shrews or elephant shrews—called by the latter name because of their long trunklike snouts—the burrowing golden moles and an aquatic fish-eating creature known as the otter shrew. A fourth family, the fantastic tenrecs, is confined to Madagascar and will be described in the chapter that deals with that island.

The only primates peculiar to Africa are the three families of lemurs found on the island of Madagascar. The mainland lorises and all of the African apes and monkeys belong to families shared with Asia.

Africa has a lot of very peculiar rodents that are found nowhere else. The scaly-tailed squirrels, for example, although in habits and body form the counterpart of the New World flying squirrels, are not really squirrels at all. Their exact relationships are in doubt. They are small, furry, big-eyed gliders that do their gliding on folds of skin stretched between the fore and hind legs of either side. The skin fold goes on around behind and can be stretched between the two hind legs too. The undersurface near the base of the tail is covered with heavy scales put on in a herringbone pattern.

Another of the rodent families restricted to Africa is that of the jumping hare, or springhaas, as the Afrikaners call it. The springhaas is about a foot long, not counting a one-foot-long tail, and has huge hind legs which it uses in hopping like a kangaroo when frightened. It is distributed from Kenya south to the Cape. It eats roots and some other vegetation, and lives in complicated burrows that may have half a dozen openings or more. Jumping hares sometimes travel 10 or 20 miles in foraging or to find water left standing after distant rains.

Perhaps the oddest family of African rodents is that of the mole rats. Although once thought to be related to the porcupine, the family has recently been placed in a separate suborder. Whatever the degree of the taxonomic distinctness the group may have achieved, there can be no doubt that one of its members is one of the wonders of the world. This is the naked mole rat.

The naked mole rat is found in open arid country in Somalia, northern Kenya and eastern Ethiopia. It spends its life underground in permanent burrows, the entrances to which are marked by craterlike piles of earth. It gathers in small colonies, easily located by these craters. Its food is mainly roots, and it probably never drinks water.

In the prime of life the naked mole rat is an incredibly amorphous-looking animal. It is almost three and a half inches long from its huge front teeth, which the lips and cheeks do not even begin to hide, to the base of its tail. It is almost completely hairless and unpigmented, and practically without eyes and external ears. Its movements are mostly a larval sort of wriggling and squirming, like those of a just-born animal. In fact, it looks very much like a fetus turned out into the world too soon. Perhaps the naked mole rat was derived by the simple process of suppressing embryonic development, so as to keep the finished product a hairless, blind and almost earless wriggler, for whatever adaptive advantage these traits might bring to underground life. Among many cave animals certain organs deteriorate, and the explanation seems to be that they simply retrogress from lack of selective maintenance. But that may not be the entire story. In the burrowing animals, loss of eyes and external ears may be positively advantageous. If you do not have these, you do not get sand in them, for instance.

The mole rat, feeble as it seems, is an industrious digger. One of its surprising attributes is that much of its digging is done with the huge incisor teeth. Moles and pocket gophers have their forelegs strikingly modified for digging, but those of the naked mole rat lack this spadelike adaptation. They seem to be used mainly for easier scratching and for kicking dirt backward in the tunnel and out of its mouth while the hard work of excavation is mostly done with the teeth. When the teeth and forefeet have dislodged and passed back a certain amount of earth, the mole rat pushes its tail stiffly downward into the pile and uses it as a prop while kicking the accumulated dirt back out of the hole with the free hind feet.

There are about 16 other known species of rodents that belong to three families found in Africa alone. These are the rock rats and the big, edible cane rats, both related to the porcupine and New World guinea pigs, and the gundis, the relationships of which are in doubt.

Another group of mammals almost but not wholly restricted to Africa, and widely distributed there, is the rabbit-sized, small-eared, tailless hyraxes. There are three genera of them, and all the species are African except one which ranges into Asia. They are in an order all their own but are placed close to the Proboscidea, which means that the elephants and these little hyraxes, although about as different-looking as mammals can be, are probably one another's nearest living kin.

A FAMILY with similar geographic range—mainly African but with one species reaching Asia—is that of the hyenas. A hyena is a far more extraordinary animal than it looks. It appears to be merely a bit odd and shifty, like a kind of irresponsible dog. But it is not a dog at all, or even kin to the dogs. It is actually a sort of cat, or more correctly, a relative of the civets and mongooses, which are cats unable to draw in their claws. The hyena is, as I said, a peculiar animal. It has a broad face, round ears, sloping hindquarters and a moth-eaten coat. It makes its living not so much by competing with vultures for carrion, as the safarists usually say, but by cracking up bones. The terrifically heavy, powerful jaws and teeth of a hyena can crush the bones of all but the most ponderous animals. This diet of bones sometimes makes the dung of hyenas limy-white, and because the animals tend to travel on designated trails and to defecate along the way, some hyena paths become whitewashed by the droppings of the travelers. Fossil bits of hyena dung have been found in Europe, many

SUBTERRANEAN DIGGERS IN SAVANNA AND DESERT

A small nose poked momentarily out of the ground to eject dirt from a tunnel is all that one is apt to see of three common African mammals. At the top is the golden mole, a five-inch subterranean insectivore with beautiful tawny fur. It uses its hard snout for digging and breaking up the soil. The two others are rodents; they dig with their extra-large front teeth. The East African mole rat (center) is 10 inches long, and the almost blind, almost hairless naked mole rat (bottom), a desert dweller, is not quite four inches long. It is a most energetic digger, ejecting earth from its burrow in tiny spurts like a miniature volcano erupting.

of them in lairs used thousands of years ago by European hyenas now extinct.

The hyena is strange in other ways. Its voice is one of the wildest in the world. It is not as reverberating as the voice of the lion or elephant, or as poignant as the trumpeting of the sandhill crane, but for eerie oddity it has no equal anywhere. Another weird thing about hyenas is that the sex organs of the males and females look just about alike—so much so in fact that some people have been led to conclude that hyenas change their sex from time to time. One reliable-seeming man records that his pet hyena became the father of one litter of pups, and then was the mother of another. This is clearly a matter that requires somebody's careful attention. Related to the hyenas is the aardwolf, a small, meek animal that has been put into a separate subfamily, Protelinae. The aardwolf's principal food is termites.

Of the well-known circus-type or animal-cracker animals, the only ones that can qualify as peculiarly African are the giraffe and the hippopotamus. Both belong to exclusively African families, and each is remarkable for its great size. The giraffe is the tallest animal on earth, and the hippo is the third heaviest. The hippopotamus has a lot of other curious traits too, and some of these will be revealed in Chapter 2. The giraffe is a bizarrely modified animal and it has a living relative that seems to show an intermediate stage in the evolution toward that bizarre condition. The relative is the okapi. The okapi looks like a partly evolved giraffe and gives the impression of simply having stopped an old family trend toward length of leg and neck before it got as extreme as it did in the giraffe proper. Today the okapi lives in the rain forest, and the big giraffe lives in savanna country. Each is obviously more suited to its own habitat than the other would be.

I am not trying to say that the okapi is the ancestor of the tall giraffe. The okapi is ancestral only to its own calves, and in its own ways is as specialized an animal as the giraffe is. But all the same, having the two animals there in Africa illustrating two steps in a fantastic adaptive trend is very satisfying.

As exciting as the fauna of Africa is—or *was* when the first explorers got there—its zenith was probably passed long ago in Pliocene or Pleistocene times. The Africa of the recent geologic past was a splendid show indeed, and the climax of the show was the most earthshaking event in all the history of the earth. It was the humanization of the primates, the coming of man, the emergence of a novel adaptive plan that made its bearer unable to live without remodeling the world. Through the years of painstaking and imaginative work by Louis and Mary Leakey at Olduvai Gorge in Tanganyika, and by others in South Africa, the cradle of humanity has been shown to be not Asia, as was previously thought, but Africa. The time of human existence has been put back perhaps as much as an additional million years and fossil men have been shown against a background of environmental detail never revealed before. These shadowy figures, and the things that have been learned about the conditions of their lives and the creatures they lived among, have furnished the first glimpse of the earliest fossil men as living beings. These discoveries have stirred scholars in many fields to extend and interpret the dramatic findings, and a growing barrage of inquiry is being directed at problems of African paleoecology. The decade coming is sure to reveal more about the origins of African men and beasts than has been learned in all the years since the Portuguese explorer Vasco da Gama made his epic voyage around the continent on his way to India in 1497.

THE FIRST GIRAFFE EVER SEEN IN BRITAIN, A GIFT IN 1827 FROM MOHAMED ALI, PASHA OF EGYPT, IS COMMEMORATED IN THIS PAINTING

Discovering Africa

So little was known of Africa for so long that the 18th Century satirist Jonathan Swift could write, "Geographers in Afric maps Make savage pictures fill their gaps, And o'er inhabitable downs Place elephants in place of towns." But with a rush of exploration in the 19th Century, the Africa of imagination gave way to an Africa of reality, stranger by far than any fantasy had ever made it.

VASCO DA GAMA

Gaining a Foothold

Up to the 15th Century, Europeans knew practically nothing about Africa south of the Sahara. Then a little information began to trickle in from Portuguese voyagers who dared to sail farther and farther south along the western coast. In 1487 Bartholomew Diaz, blown off course by storms, actually rounded the Cape of Good Hope and became the first European to venture part way up the east coast. Ten years later Vasco da Gama (*left*) sailed almost the entire length of the east coast before striking out across the Indian Ocean. In establishing a sea route to the rich Orient, da Gama's voyage underscored the importance of Africa as a stopping-off place and led to the exploitation of coastal areas by European powers. But even as late as the 18th Century, Africa was still a continent known mostly in outline.

CAPE TOWN, founded in 1652 by the Dutch East India Company as a supply center for Asia-bound ships, was already an important port when this picture was painted in 1720.

UNEXPLORED
DIAZ
DA GAMA

AFRICA IN 1487 was practically all terra incognita. Only in the northern deserts and along the Red Sea in the east had Arabs opened it up. Gradually the coast was explored in the wake of Diaz and da Gama.

NILE

L. VICTORIA

L. TANGANYIKA

A ROLY-POLY ELEPHANT and other strangely shaped beasts show what restricted knowledge Europeans had of African wildlife as late as 1604, when this engraving appeared in a book of voyages and travels.

CAPE TOWN TODAY sprawls from Table Mountain to Table Bay. Supposedly 300 ships have sunk in the bay, victims over the past 300 years of the violent gales that rip across the southern tip of Africa.

JAMES BRUCE (1730-1794)

TWO WHO TRIED

The modern era of African exploration may be said to have begun in 1768, when James Bruce, a Scot with a love of adventure and an eye for fame, set himself the task of finding the source of the Nile. Apparently not even the ancient Egyptians knew where the river rose. What Bruce—"a mere private Briton" dressed as an Arab *(above)*—found two years later, however, was not *the* source, but that of a tributary, the Blue Nile, visited over a century before by a Portuguese Jesuit. Anticlimactic as this was, his travels excited imaginations, and in 1795 another Scot, Mungo Park *(below)*, went in search of the Niger, a river few if any Europeans had ever seen. "Worn by sickness, exhausted with hunger," he found it, but was too weak to go on. Returning in 1805, he drowned the next year trying to reach the mouth.

MUNGO PARK (1771-1806)

20

RICHARD BURTON, an adventurer in rebellion against the mores of Victorian England, could speak and read 29 languages.

The Nile's Sources Found

Not until about 100 years ago was the 2,000-year-old mystery of the Nile's source—or rather sources—solved. How they were found is primarily the story of three men and one woman. It begins with Richard Burton and John Speke, who in 1858, half-starved and ill, discovered Lake Tanganyika. Burton was sure that this was the source, but Speke, bearing on while Burton stayed behind in camp, made another discovery, Lake Victoria, and became equally convinced that it was the source. Unable to agree, the men fell out. Two years later, Speke returned to Africa with James Grant and checked out his theory. Going home, they ran into Samuel and Florence Baker, who had come in search of them. The Bakers, disappointed not to have shared Speke's discovery, went on, and as their reward "for the years of tenacity with which we have toiled through Africa," found an additional source, Lake Albert.

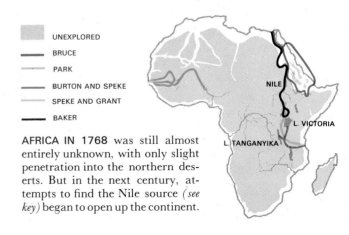

	UNEXPLORED
	BRUCE
	PARK
	BURTON AND SPEKE
	SPEKE AND GRANT
	BAKER

AFRICA IN 1768 was still almost entirely unknown, with only slight penetration into the northern deserts. But in the next century, attempts to find the Nile source *(see key)* began to open up the continent.

JOHN SPEKE, despite his mode of conveyance here, is remembered for his endurance. On his third trip to Africa, he walked from the coast to the Nile, a distance of more than 1,000 miles.

SAMUEL AND FLORENCE BAKER, a wealthy couple, in striving to find the source of the Nile ignored all vicissitudes, "determined to die upon the road rather than return defeated."

THE SOURCE OF SOME OF THE NILE'S WATERS IS RAIN THAT FALLS ON THE MOSSES OF THE RUWENZORI RANGE WEST OF LAKE VICTORIA

DAVID LIVINGSTONE

MEETING A CHIEF, Livingstone declined to sit on the ground. The chief had a tusk brought for a seat, then gave it to him.

A Man with a Purpose

No man did more to open up Africa than David Livingstone, a strong-willed Scot who went to Africa in 1841 as a missionary, became a great explorer and wound up a kind of statesman. His prime motive was neither evangelism nor exploration, but the suppression of the slave trade, which in the year 1835 alone had accounted for the export of around 150,000 Africans. With this end in mind, he sought to "open a path for commerce and Christianity," and in the course of three major trips, each of several years' duration, he followed the Zambezi to its mouth and made such major discoveries as Victoria Falls and Lake Nyasa. He always traveled slowly, eager to know the people he encountered, treating them with kindness and exercising "the utmost forbearance" toward them. On his last journey, he disappeared into the bush for three years and was not heard from until the journalist Henry Stanley found him, a haggard, sick, aging man. Once again he disappeared, this time to die. "We seem immortal," he had written, "till our work is done."

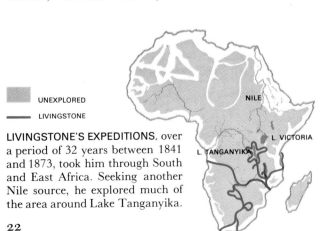

UNEXPLORED

LIVINGSTONE

LIVINGSTONE'S EXPEDITIONS, over a period of 32 years between 1841 and 1873, took him through South and East Africa. Seeking another Nile source, he explored much of the area around Lake Tanganyika.

MAULED BY A LION, Livingstone had his arm torn. Later he joked, "I was wondering what part of me he would eat first."

CARRIED BY A PORTER, Livingstone, a few months before his death, was too weak to walk through a rain-flooded swamp.

LIVINGSTONE'S INITIALS were carved inside a hollow baobab in 1858 and discovered in 1958 by a photographer, who persuaded the Mozambique government to make the tree a monument.

A RAINBOW forms a narrow bridge across one of Livingstone's most spectacular discoveries—Victoria Falls. Sailing in a tiny boat to an island at the lip of the falls, he landed and crept "with awe to the verge."

HENRY MORTON STANLEY

MEETING LIVINGSTONE at the end of a 236-day trek, Stanley suppresses "feelings that were well-nigh uncontrollable," doffs his freshly chalked sun helmet and says, "Doctor Livingstone, I presume?"

SHOOTING RAPIDS in the Congo, Stanley sits surrounded by porters. On this expedition, his second, he lost 114 members through such causes as drowning, dysentery, fever, opium, starvation and murder.

WAGENIA TRIBESMEN STILL PADDLE THROUGH RAPIDS IN THE CONGO AS IN STANLEY'S DAY, CLOSE BY THE FALLS STANLEY DISCOVERED

THE RUWENZORI RANGE, discovered by Stanley in 1888, stands lost in the clouds. It proved to be the Mountains of the Moon mentioned by Ptolemy in the Second Century.

A Man in Search of Himself

Sent out by the *New York Herald* to find Livingstone, Henry Morton Stanley did more than that: he found himself. Illegitimate, unwanted, he had run away from a Welsh workhouse and made his way to New Orleans. There he met up with a kindly man who gave him his name. In succession he joined the Confederate Army, was captured, enlisted in the Union Army, was discharged, joined the Navy and deserted. At 24 he was a roving reporter, but not until his meeting with Livingstone six years later did he discover his true vocation—exploration. Stanley carried on Livingstone's work after the missionary's death, but his aggressive manner and opportunism made him unpopular. He was loved by some Victorians, snubbed by most.

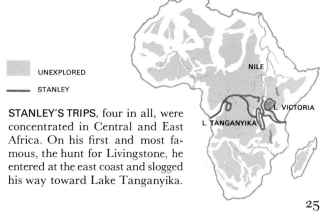

UNEXPLORED

STANLEY

STANLEY'S TRIPS, four in all, were concentrated in Central and East Africa. On his first and most famous, the hunt for Livingstone, he entered at the east coast and slogged his way toward Lake Tanganyika.

25

HUNTER OF THE OLD SCHOOL, Teddy Roosevelt on his 1909-1910 safari shot animals for food or exhibition in museums.

CROSSING A RIVER, Roosevelt rides out front, rifle in hand. "Our tents, our accommodations generally," he complained,

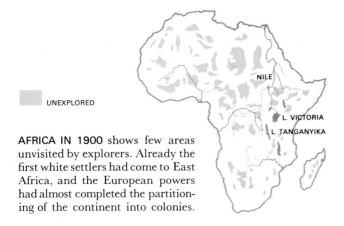

UNEXPLORED

AFRICA IN 1900 shows few areas unvisited by explorers. Already the first white settlers had come to East Africa, and the European powers had almost completed the partitioning of the continent into colonies.

Fair Game

After the explorers, came the hunters—and still they come. Some were merely ruthless, tempted by the abundance of the game to get as big a bag as possible. Others, like Theodore Roosevelt (*above, left*), respected the animals and were more interested in observing them than in slaughtering them, more eager for the experience of the hunt than the trophies. In Roosevelt's day, hunters still had to go on foot, mule or horse and drink from mudholes, and all

A GAME SMILE

GRINNING BROADLY, movie cowboy Roy Rogers poses with, from left to right, a kudu, a porcupine, a nyala, a lesser sable antelope, a warthog and a waterbuck, part of his bag on a 1962 safari in Mozambique. Object of the three-week-long hunt was

"seemed almost too comfortable for men who knew camp life
. . . on the great plains, in the Rockies, and in the North woods."

HUNTER OF THE NEW SCHOOL. Arthur Godfrey disembarks
from a helicopter used to spot game and herd it toward rifles
—and to shorten an elephant kill from a week to two hours.

equipment had to be transported on the heads and
shoulders of porters. But with the introduction of
the automobile to the African plains, the picture
soon changed, and luxury and ease became the key-
note *(right and below)*. The heyday of the luxury
safari was reached in the '20s, when on some hunts
tents covered as much as an acre of ground, gen-
erators provided electricity, great feasts were prepared and fine wines were served with each course.

not big game but rare antelope, the skins of which were sent home for mounting as
trophies. The safari, on which Rogers and another client were accompanied by two
white hunters, included two Land Rovers, 25 natives, hot water and a refrigerator.

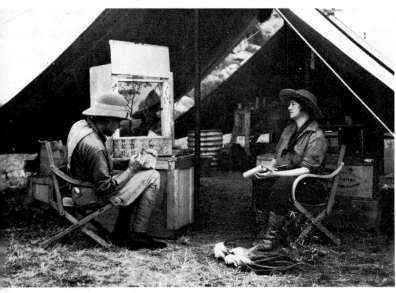

HUNTING LIONS WITH A CAMERA, Carl Akeley stands in the touring car at right. Akeley's camera, his own invention, was the first of its kind for making films of animals in action.

AN OSTRICH BLIND, photographed by Carl Akeley in Kenya, conceals the man inside well enough to allow him, in the days before telephoto lenses, to photograph large game close up.

IN THE FIELD shortly before his death, Akeley goes over the model for an exhibit in the proposed African Hall. With him is his wife, who later assumed leadership of the expedition.

Bringing Africa Home

As wild Africa began to disappear, driven back everywhere, some men were moved to preserve as much of it as possible, in parks, in zoos, on film and in museums. The man who did perhaps most to fix and record this fleeting Africa was Carl Akeley, naturalist, conservationist, photographer, inventor, sculptor and taxidermist. His method of mounting animals made it possible for museums to display them for the first time in natural poses.

Akeley's experience with Africa began early—

AKELEY'S DREAM FULFILLED, the African Hall of the American Museum of Natural History attracts two million visitors a year. Displayed on the two levels are 28 habitat groups, perfect

and dramatically. On his first trip, in 1896, he was attacked by a wounded leopard, which he wrestled to the ground and killed with his own hands, jamming his hand down its throat to cut off its breathing. On his second trip, 10 years later, he was mauled by an enraged elephant. But so strongly did he love Africa that he was able, while recovering from his wounds, to envision a great African Hall for the American Museum of Natural History in New York (*below*), a hall that would "tell the story of jungle peace." During the second of two collecting expeditions for the hall, Akeley worked with a zeal that enabled him to collect in eight months the material for seven habitat groups, but as the price for his accomplishment he became ill with fever and exhaustion. No man to give in, he insisted on going to gorilla country, and there, high in the Mufumbiro Mountains, in what he considered to be the most beautiful spot in the world, he died. His body was buried on the mountainside.

down to the leaves of the plants among which the animals stand. The bronze statues flanking the elephant group were sculpted by Akeley himself, who died before work on the hall had properly begun. Some of the elephants were first shaped in clay, then plaster molds were made and casts taken, and finally the preserved skins were drawn over the adhesive-coated casts.

SPAIN

ATLANTIC OCEAN

Mediterranean Sea

SAUDI-

Atlas Mountains

A

SAHARA

Qattara Depression

SAHARA

F

Red Sea

Niger

Sénégal

L. Chad

R

Nile

White Nile

Blue Nile

Volta

L. Albert

L. Rudolf

Gulf of Guinea

Ubangi

I

Congo

Sankuru

Congo

Lake Victoria

Kasai

Cuango

L. Tanganyika

Cuanco

L. Nyasa

Zambezi

Cunene

KALAHARI

Limpopo

Orange

Drakensberg Mts.

Mozambique

ATLANTIC

Desert

Steppe, Wooded Steppe

Savannah & Grassland

Tropical Rain Forest

Tall Grassland

Mediterranean and Cape Scrub

Swamp

Park or Preserve

A Continent Revealed

The Africa dealt with in this book is all the land south of the Sahara, which to a large extent is an enormous plateau. The map at left shows the vegetation of the region today, plus the major rivers, lakes, deserts and mountain ranges. Contrary to what most people suppose, Africa is not dominated by rain forest but by savanna and grasslands, the haunt of many of its biggest and most familiar animals. As a glance at the map and key will tell, the vegetation follows a relatively simple pattern, reflecting variations in temperature and rainfall. The portion of East Africa in the square is enlarged below. It represents the region to which the greater part of the book is devoted and to which many of the early explorers were drawn. Here, among other features, are the Great Rift Valley, an enormous cleavage in the earth's crust; the great lakes, including the second deepest in the world, Tanganyika; and many of the finest national parks and reserves (outlined in white), the last fastnesses of African wildlife.

GREATER FLAMINGOS attend their eggs in the midst of a colony of 20,000 at Lake Elmenteita, Kenya. The total East African population numbers less than a million—far below the three to five million lesser flamingos, whose nesting grounds these larger birds sometimes share.

2

Life in Lakes and Rivers

WHEN the early explorers began to open up Africa, it was mostly the waterways they traveled, the Nile, Niger, Zambezi and Congo rivers and the hundreds of lesser streams, and the great lakes of the eastern plateau region. In those days, the banks of the lakes and rivers were gathering places for the big mammals. Great herds of elephants, buffaloes and antelopes came down to drink, to bathe or to graze the bottomland grass, and the carnivores came to prey upon them. Now, except along such enchanted and cherished bits of water as the Kazinga Channel or the Victoria Nile, it is no longer possible to see much of the fauna from a boat. Nowhere in all Africa can one count 800 elephants along one mile of shore, as Livingstone did on the Shire River in Nyasaland (now Malawi). An occasional crocodile or band of hippos, both of which must live in the water or not at all, still brings bursts of excitement to any voyage that runs beyond the sterile abodes of man. But that is about it, and even that is rare outside the limits of the game preserves.

Nevertheless, travel on African rivers and lakes can still be a fine fiesta for a naturalist. There are still the incomparable African fishes down under the hull, for instance, and the magnificent African water birds to see. Even in most places

33

outside the protected areas, the water birds of the continent remain a spectacular asset. Grebes, cormorants and darters are not often out of view for long, and kingfishers still rattle ahead of any boat in a spectrum of sizes, some fishing singly, some in little bands. There is a gratifying diversity of ducks, geese, cranes, herons, storks, ibises and spoonbills, and a flock of African flamingos flying over against the African sky is one of the great sights of the whole continent. Jaçanas, rails and moorhens run over the lily pads; plovers, snipe, curlews and sandpipers gather on the spits and bars; gulls, terns and pelicans cruise the larger lakes and rivers. Fish eagles and fish hawks squeal and bicker in the sky; wagtails putter about clean flats; weaverbirds nest in the papyrus; martins and swallows dip and swoop over the surface of the water.

I F the African fishes are any less exciting than the water birds to the river traveler it is only because they rarely come out and fly and walk the shores. The fresh-water fishes of the Ethiopian region are one of the zoological marvels of the world. Something was said about these fishes in Chapter 1, but not nearly enough. There is one ichthyological wonder in Africa, for example, which when more is known about it will almost surely become a classic case for the study of evolution in action. This is the exuberant speciation of the fishes of the family Cichlidae in the lakes of the Great Rift Valley. These lakes hold some of the most engrossing evolutionary mysteries to be found in the earth.

For some reason lakes in many parts of the world not only are peculiarly rich repositories of endemics—of kinds of animals found there and nowhere else—but tend also to have in them large groups of closely related forms known as "species flocks." Species flocks are produced by what is known as "explosive evolution." The process is by no means well understood, but the African lakes contain some astonishing examples of these speciation orgies. There is in Lake Nyasa a genus of cichlids that has over a hundred species in it. All of them are apparently more closely related to each other than to any other fishes anywhere else in the world; that is to say, they have all descended from a single ancestral species and evidently they all evolved right there in the lake. This is the biggest species flock that has ever been found, the most graphic example of explosive evolution ever known.

The African cichlids fascinate the biologist because they show evolution in action. There are other fishes in Africa that show evolution stopped. These are the bichirs and lungfishes. Lungfishes are not confined to the African region. They occur in Australia and in South America also. Once a diverse and successful group, they are now almost at the end of their evolutionary rope; there are only three surviving genera of the whole major category to which they belong. Lungfishes are not the stock from which the amphibians—the first land vertebrates—arose. They are not far from it; but their own venture in land-living only went so far as to allow them to live through times of drought. When its watery environment dries up, the African lungfish goes into the mud. It lays down a cocoon of slime about itself, and this hardens into an impervious shell. The cocoon has an opening at the top that connects with the outside by a vertical chimney, and in a desultory sort of way the encysted fish breathes through this. In this refuge the lungfish can stay alive for as long as four years. It burns its muscle tissue to keep a quiet metabolism under way and simply lives with its metabolic wastes—which may involve toleration of concentrations of urea a hundred times higher than those that most vertebrate animals can stand. During a long retreat of this sort, a lungfish becomes a mere mummy of its former

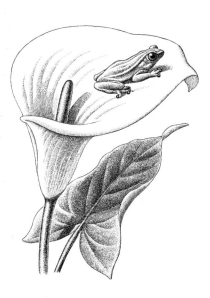

HIDING IN A LILY BLOOM

Colored an ivory white to match the hue of the arum lily, this small frog spends its days squatting motionless and virtually invisible deep down in the lily's throat. It keeps its legs, which are pink, tucked underneath itself for concealment and moves only to seize small insects and spiders attracted by the lily's pollen. As night comes on, the arum lily frog's body darkens, and it ventures forth for more active hunting. Although it is only an inch long, it is a powerful jumper and can leap a foot and a half straight up.

self, losing not only much of its own weight but even some of its length as well. When the water comes back into its world, however, the lungfish is prepared to resume living again, and to reproduce and leave behind other drought-resistant lungfishes.

African lungfishes may reach lengths up to seven feet and weights of over a hundred pounds. They are good to eat and are much sought by the Africans. They are taken with lines, nets and spears; when waters recede and leave the fish encysted, they are dug out with mattocks and hoes. It looks peculiar to see an African fishing with a hoe. It is not as sporting as casting a dry fly for trout, but for dry-season lungfish fishing, the hoe is the practical tackle.

Another very old group of fishes, wholly endemic to Africa, is that of the polypterids: the bichirs and reed fishes. These make up a separate order not known, even as fossils, anywhere outside Africa. There are two genera and 11 species of them, distributed in tropical Africa northward into the Nile. Bichirs are closely related to primitive fishes of the Paleozoic. They have air bladders which, like those of lungfishes and amphibians, connect with the pharynx by a ventral opening, and they evidently breathe some air, though they cannot live out of water. A characteristic not shared with other old fishes of the Paleozoic is the presence of from five to 18 little fins arranged along the back. It is these that are referred to in the generic name *Polypterus*, which means "many-fins." The other genus of this group is *Calamoichthys*, the reed fish, found in the rivers of tropical West Africa.

Besides these incredibly old types of vertebrate life, the African fauna has 11 other endemic fresh-water fish families. Some of these are almost as old as the bichirs and have no doubt occupied Africa since times when their body designs were the latest thing. Others are far more modern and have near kin living in other regions of the world. One of the important endemic African families is the Mormyridae, the group that includes the curious elephant-snout fishes, extraordinarily droll-looking animals with long snouts drawn out as probing tubes for catching bottom-dwelling invertebrates. Related to them is the electric fish of the Nile, an elongated, spindle-shaped fish with a long snout, a tiny mouth, a finely tapered tail and a continuous dorsal fin which moves with graceful undulations to push the fish smoothly along through the water.

Although the eyes of the electric fish are small, it is an active and accurate pursuer of the small fishes upon which it preys, depending on intermittent weak charges of electricity to help it locate them. Other kinds of fishes, including the African electric catfish, emit heavy discharges that are capable of killing or stunning the animals they eat, but whether they electrocute them for that purpose is not known.

M ost casual travelers on African lakes or rivers might never come face to face with the scientific mystery of the cichlid species flocks. They even might miss the quietly fantastic feats of the electric fish. The African fishes would nevertheless impress themselves upon the voyager in more obvious ways. One of the highlights of river travel is the elaborate diversity of fishing techniques and equipment that one sees in passing, especially along the Congo, where the variety and complexity of traps and nets probably cannot be matched in the fresh waters of the world. If one's interest in wildlife is mainly gastronomic, then trying to decide objectively whether, as some claim, certain of the cichlids of the great lakes are really the most succulent fresh-water fish on earth will add zest to one's travels. For anglers, Africa also offers other superlatives to test. One is

TROTTING ON A LILY PAD

Scurrying about on lily pads and other floating vegetation in African marshes, and often looking as if they could actually walk on water, are the jaçana and black crake. Both rely on constant motion and extremely long toes, and always seem to be stepping onto another lily pad just as the first one is about to sink under them. Even if it did, it would not matter; both are excellent swimmers and dive to escape enemies. The crake (lower picture) has learned to roll up the edges of lily pads with its bill to get at the aquatic insects hidden underneath.

the tiger fish, a ferocious and dynamic relative of the New World piranha. On a line the tiger fish can hold its head up among bonefish, tarpon or wahoo, and by patriotic Africa hands it is said to outperform all others. The other is the Nile perch, a strong predator that reaches weights of 350 pounds or more. Trolling or casting for Nile perch in the fast waters of the Victoria Nile below Murchison Falls is a fine sport in a magnificent setting. Landing one of these immense fish is especially satisfying to a North American, because they look so much like a gigantic bass.

Africa is also famous for its spectacular array of catfishes. There are 250 kinds there, belonging to seven different families, three of which are endemic. African catfishes often reach weights of over 100 pounds, and one caught in Lake Edward weighed 276 pounds. This was a clariid catfish, a member of a group that has supplementary respiratory organs on each side of the head behind the regular gills. They can live a long time out of water and even slither about for some distance on land. Franz and Elinor Sauer came back from South-West Africa with a fine tale about clariid catfishes. One rainy night while talking with a farmer who was putting them up they heard a sudden din of dogs barking in front of the farmhouse. Everybody rushed out to see what the trouble was and found a shoal of catfish moving up the wet road, heading for some place known only to themselves and putting the dogs into a fearful lather with their unorthodox behavior. The same catfish family includes not only giant species but also the peculiar West African eel cats, which may be a foot long and no bigger around than a pencil.

Other arresting ichthyological sights in Africa are the fresh-water puffers, which inflate themselves to sphericality when taken out of the water; the squeakers, which are catfishes, some of them able to swim about upside down; and the butterfly fish, which is a fresh-water flying fish found in the Congo basin.

I N the first chapter the hippopotamus was named as one of the genuinely distinctive animals of Africa. It is. Actually there are two kinds of living hippopotamuses, the familiar behemoth and the West African pygmy form, which is no bigger than a good-sized hog and belongs to another genus. Within the relatively recent past, this pygmy hippo, or a very similar one, was common in Madagascar. In the Pliocene, hippopotamuses occurred in Europe and Asia. Nowadays, however, the family is found only in Africa. The range in historic times was from the delta of the Nile to the Cape of Good Hope. When Europeans first arrived at the Cape, there were hippos in a lake in what is now the heart of Cape Town.

Of all the big animals of Africa, the hippopotamus was probably more quickly decimated during the early days of colonization than any other. The rivers were the highways into the land. The great, gregarious water horses crowded together unsuspecting on the mudbanks and stared and snorted at the passing boats. They were shot, at first, for idle fun or to feed a passing expedition. Later, however, advancing colonization and big public-works projects put big gangs of Africans to work, and these were fed on dried meat. The most readily available meat was that of the hippopotamus, and in places the animal was wholly wiped out. Along most African rivers, however, small herds can now and then still be seen, and in some of the national parks hippos are spectacularly abundant.

A mature hippopotamus may weigh up to 8,000 pounds and stand about four-and-a-half feet high at the shoulder. The young are born singly, after a

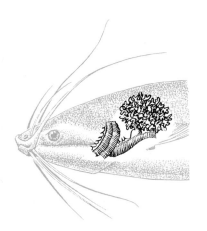

AIR-BREATHING CATFISH

Thanks to the treelike organ, shown in the cutaway above, which acts as a supplement to the gills and greatly increases the surface area available for bringing oxygen into contact with the blood, a clariid catfish can live for several days out of water. This enables it to travel from one pond or river to another during dry seasons. These journeys (below) are usually made at night by as many as 30 fish at a time, wriggling like snakes through the grass, grunting faintly as they go. How they are able to detect another water source to head for is not known.

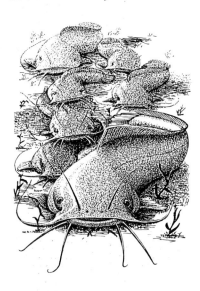

gestation period of eight months. Birth takes place in the water, as does suckling, the nursing youngsters coming up periodically for air. Most of the daylight hours are spent in the water or basking on mudbanks. As ponderous and stubby-legged as it is, the hippopotamus is a powerful swimmer and is also able to walk about on the bottoms of lakes or down the beds of streams, coming up now and then to breathe. One of the arresting sights of the African national parks is the hippos swimming in the clear waters of Mzima Springs in Tsavo National Park in Kenya.

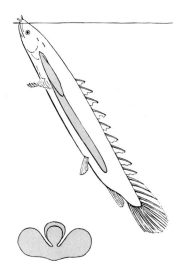

THE cavernous mouth and ponderous tusks of the hippopotamus suggest that it feeds by uprooting aquatic plants or that it chomps up great volumes of floating vegetation. This is not the case. An astonishing thing that I have only recently learned about hippopotamuses is that they are efficient and inveterate grazers. The water is merely their protection and privacy, not the main source of their food. At night all the hippos go ashore and push their vast muzzles into the turf, and clip grass as neatly as a sheep. They eat 50 or more pounds dry weight of grass during a night. They travel as far as five miles back inland, among the kobs, oribis, hartebeests, buffaloes and elephants. When their numbers become unnaturally large in some of the national parks, the damage they do to the vegetation along the rivers gets to be an important management problem.

The hippopotamus has a voice that is big but not easy to describe. It is not a sustained roar of a stature that an animal its size might promise. It is a repertoire of grunts, groans, ground-shaking rumbles and short, petulant bellows. One standard utterance is a series of rumbling aow-aow-aow-aows. The greatest noise is made when there is a fight, such as took place one night across the upper Shire River from our camp in Nyasaland. For a while it made sleep impossible. The next day I paddled across to look over the scene of the disturbance. The papyrus, reeds and water lettuce were beaten down over an area about a hundred feet across, but the contestants were nowhere to be seen. A day later, I went over again and found a dead hippo, floating belly up, with hundreds of catfishes assembled underneath him. At great cost to our senses of smell an African and I moored our boat to the slippery, bloated bobbing body and with some difficulty cut the big tusks out of the jaws. I took them home to my children.

Although the record is somewhat emotional, there is no doubt that the hippopotamus can be a danger to human life under certain conditions. Canoes are sometimes overturned by hippos, and anyone who stands between one of them and the water, or between a mother and her calf, is likely to find himself in trouble. The unpredictable nature of this animal is suggested by an incident related by Sir Samuel Baker in his *Wild Beasts and Their Ways*. A herd of cattle being driven across a river was attacked by hippopotamuses. As Baker watched, several of the cows were seized and dragged underwater. They never reappeared. Baker attributed the attack to "sheer rage" on the part of the hippos, perhaps aroused by the violation of their territory.

The hippopotamus often descends streams into salt water. According to C. S. Stokes, "usually crocodiles, sharks and hippos live peacefully together when they share a stretch of water." He tells of one case, however, in which five sharks attacked a hippo sleeping in St. Lucia Bay in Zululand. According to 20 witnesses who saw the fight from fishing boats, the encounter ended when the hippo "sent the sharks somersaulting into the air, one after another."

TWO OTHER AIR BREATHERS

Another solution to the problem of obtaining fresh air, and possibly a clue to how lungs evolved in land vertebrates, is shown by these fish. Each has a paired swim bladder, a gas-filled balloonlike organ (shown in color) used by many fish for controlling position in the water. But in the bichir (above) and lungfish (below) the swim bladder is connected to the throat, and fresh oxygen can be drawn into it when the fish comes to the surface to swallow air. Cross sections of the bladders show the lungfish's to be more lunglike with its elaborate inner surface.

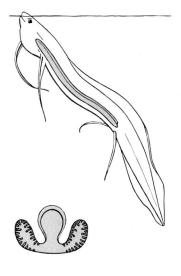

37

The greatest concentration of hippos left in Africa is probably in Queen Elizabeth National Park in Uganda, where there are 14,000 of them. Here the Nuffield Unit of Tropical Animal Ecology has embarked on the most intensive study ever made of the ecology of the hippopotamus or perhaps of any African ungulate. The investigation has already shown that the hippo population in the park is unhandily large and that the range is being seriously damaged. Annual cropping of excess hippos is being carried out to maintain stability in the riverside environment.

Of the other African ungulates, the most aquatic are the chevrotain, the river hog, the lechwe—a marsh-dwelling relative of the waterbuck, kob and reedbuck—and the sitatunga, related to the bushbuck. The sitatunga lives in papyrus swamps; if cornered it will jump into the water and swim under the surface for concealment, pushing its muzzle out to breathe. The most secretive of the aquatic mammals of Africa is the water chevrotain of the rain-forest rivers and swamps. Chevrotains are an odd group of ruminants, found today only in Asia and Africa. Hornless, they have four hoofed toes on both the front and hind feet, and look vaguely like big rodents. The upper canines of the male are long tusks. The African chevrotain is about 15 inches high at the shoulder and is brown with white spots. When surprised along the bank of a stream, it jumps into the water and disappears. Similar animals that occurred in the Eocene were not very different from the camels of that time. The obscure little chevrotain may therefore be close to the ancestors of all the ruminants.

Another aquatic mammal, not usually thought of as African but actually common in some places there, is the otter. There are two kinds in Africa, the clawless and the spotted-necked. The latter is almost wholly aquatic and seems mainly to be a lake dweller, being especially numerous in Lake Victoria. It eats fish, crustaceans and mollusks. During the several weeks I spent on the Shire River and southern Lake Nyasa, otters were for days at a time the only wild mammals that we saw. Although hunted to some extent for its skin, the spotted-necked otter probably has not been seriously affected by the spread of man. John Procter makes this cheering assessment of the outlook of the species in Lake Victoria: "Since its flesh is not eaten and its skin has so far been in comparatively slight demand the otter is not greatly molested by the natives and continues to live in what is probably near to its primeval ecological equilibrium. Highly aquatic and living in a huge fishpond, the wealth of which has so far scarcely been touched by man, many otters probably live out their lives scarcely, if ever, coming into contact with human beings." Such optimistic notes are seldom struck in accounts of African wildlife.

WHEN Africa was dark and its only roads were rivers, two big, ubiquitous, abundant creatures ranged the watercourses. One was the hippopotamus, the other was the crocodile. These two aquatic animals, one a predaceous reptile and the other a herbivorous mammal, gathered on the banks in similar basking groups, had about the same distribution in primitive Africa and now are similarly almost gone.

Although there are three species of crocodiles in Africa, it is the classic *Crocodylus niloticus*, the Nile crocodile, that everyone knows about. It ranges from the Cape of Good Hope northward to the Nile delta, and in former days occurred along the Mediterranean coast to Palestine and Syria. It is tolerant of salt water and is seen along the coast of southeastern Africa, where a report of a fight between a crocodile and a shark brings to mind the struggle

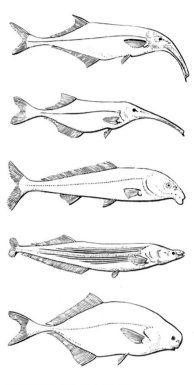

NO TWO NOSES ALIKE

Although wildly varied in appearance, the mouth parts of elephant-snout fishes are basically similar. Each fish is a bottom feeder with a tiny mouth and only a few teeth at the very end of whatever-shaped snout it may have. The top two have long beaklike noses adapted for poking between stones and plant stems. The others snuffle along on the bottom.

between sharks and a hippopotamus that I mentioned earlier. The South African sharks would seem to be an enterprising lot.

In the early days one of the awe-inspiring sights of African river travel was the aggregations of monster crocodiles that piled themselves about favored basking sites along the banks. Those assemblages have almost disappeared, and their loss is a major change in the African landscape. In three months' work along the Shire River, during which I traveled the full length of the river from Lake Nyasa to the Zambezi, I saw only one basking aggregation. To read David Livingstone's accounts of the teeming crocodiles of the Shire and then to travel the river today makes one wonder if it was really this stream that the missionary was writing about.

The depletion along the Shire River is fairly typical for most of Africa. The crocodile has now become very rare in South Africa and Kenya, and is waning nearly everywhere. There is one place, however, where big gangs of the beasts still give the shore the old grand, appalling Mesozoic look. That is along the Victoria Nile in Uganda, between Murchison Falls and Lake Albert. A section of the river runs through the Murchison Falls National Park, and although poachers molest them within the park limits, they are relatively secure and have maintained a population probably about as dense as it was in the days before rifles came to the rivers.

ONE factor in the decline of the crocodile has been the recent spread of firearms among people who for centuries have suffered from its depredations. But in the last few years the leather trade has begun an energetic ransacking of the tropical world for reptile hides. This steadily growing demand threatens various lizards and snakes with dangerous depletion and is probably most serious in the cases of various species of crocodilians.

The natural history of crocodiles has until lately been mainly hearsay or fragmentary observations of zoologists. In 1961, however, Hugh B. Cott published the results of his careful studies of crocodile ecology in Uganda—mainly on the Victoria Nile—and in Northern Rhodesia (now Zambia), Barotseland and Zululand. His data show that female crocodiles reach sexual maturity at about 19 years of age, when they are at least eight feet long. The male grows a little faster and reaches a larger maximum size. This is a much slower adolescence than that of the American alligator. As to maximum size, so much wild talk about crocodile lengths has been put into print that many zoologists have shied away from the higher figures and erred on the side of conservatism. Cott's conclusion is that the Nile crocodile reaches lengths of up to 20 feet. Its diet must change markedly with age. The young eat insects, spiders and other invertebrates, which they catch at the water's edge. In the middle years the main food is taken underwater and consists of crustaceans, fishes and mollusks. Big crocodiles eat mostly mammals and birds—and smaller crocodiles.

Many crocodilians have the odd habit of swallowing stones and other objects of no nutritional value. Various theories have been advanced to explain this. Some have thought the stones have a role in mechanical digestion, like the gizzard stones of birds. Cott, however, showed evidence that the stones may have a useful hydrostatic function. While I certainly do not question his carefully weighed conclusion, I cannot help but wonder why the American alligator should fantastically embellish the useful ballast-swallowing instinct by taking in all sorts of odd objects either light or heavy, such as fishing sinkers, shotgun shells—both charged and empty—broken porcelain, coins and pine knots.

A NET FOR EVERY FISH

Shown here are four of the literally hundreds of nets and weirs that have been developed by Africans for catching fish. The conical baskets above depend on the swift-running Congo River water to hold any fish that are swept into them.

The hand-hole basket is used in calm lake water by fishermen who walk about in the shallows. When a fish is detected with the toes, the basket is clapped down on it, and the fisherman can then reach in for it through the hole in the top.

The answer may simply be that because most alligators live where there are no small stones to swallow, they fulfill the old crocodilian ballast-urge as best they can and collect all objects heavy enough to have sunk to the bottom.

The eggs of the Nile crocodile, some 25 to 95 in number, are laid in a hole dug by the female on a spit, beach or sandy shore. The digging process has not been well observed. There is no neat mound of vegetation such as the alligator builds. There is some tendency toward colonial nesting, and Cott thinks this may have been more general before populations were reduced by hunting.

To anyone who has heard American zoologists dispute the question of parental care by the alligator, Cott's observations are very interesting indeed. The mother crocodile stays near the nest and actively guards it during incubation. She appears also to hear and to recognize the croaking of the newly hatched young buried in the nest pit and helps them emerge by pushing away the hardened soil that covers the nest. As to whether, and for how long, the mother and young stay together after going into the water, there are only scattered observations. The consensus is that the hatchlings remain with the parent for a time, and that she retains at least some of the belligerent protective attitude that she had while guarding the nest.

Cott found that, although crocodiles are so-called "cold-blooded" animals, they actually maintain a fairly constant temperature, as lizards do, by varying their behavior during the daily cycle. They pass the night in the water. Just before sunrise they go ashore, bask in the growing sunshine for a couple of hours, then move into shade or go back into the water. In the afternoon, there is another basking period of two or three hours. The basking is, of course, necessary to bring the body temperature up to the optimum level. Undue rise of temperature is controlled by the shifts into water or to shade. Cott believes that a further cooling effect may be contributed by the habit of mouth-gaping so prevalent among crocodiles on the shore—through radiation of heat by evaporation from the moist lining of the open mouth.

THE American alligator is famous for its earthshaking voice, but travelers and naturalists have had little to say of the voice of the Nile crocodile. At one time or another when I have found myself among crocodiles of great size and numbers, I have listened purposefully for their vocalizations but never was able to hear any sound other than the croaks of the young and broken snorts or grumbles by the elders. For a long time I could not make out from the literature whether the creature is capable of producing anything comparable to the alligator's roar. Now Cott has settled that matter too. He recognizes six separate sorts of crocodile songs, as follows: (1) the "yapping or croaking call" of the young; (2) a short coughing hiss uttered as part of the threat display when a crocodile is cornered and unable to escape to the water; (3) a low growl, sometimes made by a female surprised while guarding her eggs; (4) the bellow of a wounded crocodile; (5) a deep, hollow, abrupt cough made by basking males during the breeding season; (6) the full roar, only heard during the breeding season and apparently uttered only by males. This "most powerful and remarkable demonstration of a crocodile's repertoire . . . is a growing rumble, very deep in pitch, rattling, vibrant and sonorous, like distant thunder or the roll of a big drum." This description might almost equally well have been applied to the April utterance of the American alligator, which seems to me one of the great animal songs of all the world.

Anyone who has traveled an African river along which crocodiles remain has seen the curious tendency of various water birds to socialize with the forbidding gangs of the basking reptiles. Crowned cranes, great white egrets, little egrets, Egyptian and knob-billed geese, white-faced tree ducks, sacred ibises, white-collared pratincoles, pied wagtails, African skimmers and several other birds that haunt the waterside habitats may often be seen resting with crocodiles on the same sand bar or bit of shore and showing a remarkable lack of concern over their presence. Some birds—the spurwing plover and the common sand-piper—not only seem unafraid of crocodiles but actually get some of their food from them, even venturing into the gaped mouths to pick at leeches or debris, or running about the scaly back after insects of various sorts—especially tsetse flies, which often swarm over crocodiles.

T HE relationship between birds and the Nile crocodile has been known since the days of Pliny and before, although the old chronicles do not satisfactorily identify the bird species involved. One thing that has not been realized, how-ever, is that the association may not be a one-sided affair but a truly mutual-istic one, in which the bird furnishes a useful warning service in return for its foraging privileges. The arrangement appears to duplicate that between the buff-backed heron and the herds of game it associates with. The reality of such relationships is sometimes looked upon with suspicion by some zoologists be-cause they are hard to prove by experimentation. However, the accumulated, purposeful observations of careful zoologists seem to indicate that they do in fact exist. In the case of the bird associates of the crocodile, Cott says this:

Women of the Jaluo tribe in Uganda gather in a loose circle and swish large baskets back and forth, driving a school of fish into a small area where they can be scooped up. Caught fish are put in the baskets on the women's heads.

"While the commensal birds rid the crocodile of some ecto-parasites, these and other species play a far more important role in giving timely warning of danger. On countless occasions, while concealed in the hide, I have noted the reptile's immediate response to the alarm signal of birds which, of course, be-come aware of an approaching man or boat before their sleeping companions. The shrill call of a spurwing plover or water dikkop is sufficient to send most of the crocodiles stampeding into the water, while others, often the largest on the beach, will delay their departure—raising their heads and looking for the cause of alarm, before following in retreat. Even the craning of a goose's neck, or the flurry of a sandpiper, provides a sufficient stimulus, and all the crocodiles are at once alert and ready to leave.

"In the capacity of watch-dog, the spurwing plover takes pride of place in Uganda. While other species fly from the grounds when alarmed, the plovers will often remain, fluttering over the reptiles' backs and uttering the urgent notes—"quick, quick, quick"—as though to ensure that their charges are awake. Curzon saw one of these plovers dash itself two or three times against the head of a sleeping crocodile that he had surprised at close range. Such behavior might appear incredible, were it not known that under similar circumstances oxpeck-ers react in the same way towards the rhinoceros—even attempting to arouse an animal that has been shot."

Another Jaluo trap is the nonreturn bas-ket which is anchored in still water and baited to entice fish in through the hole at one end. Once in, they cannot find their way out. Small fish wander on into the second trap and are caught there.

In the case of the old crocodiles, the need of these dreadnoughts for a warn-ing system against any natural enemy is hard to conceive, and the reaction to the alarm of the birds may be either a holdover from their vulnerable youth or a response learned individually since the advent of firearms. By contrast, the enemies of the young are legion. The hatchlings are about a foot long, and the eggs are as nourishing as any eggs. Both are a staple in the diet of some ani-mals and furnish occasional bonanzas for many others. Marabou storks, fish eagles and fish hawks are known to prey on the hatchlings; in fact they may be eaten by nearly any fish-eating bird, mammal or reptile big enough to rend or swallow one. Perhaps the most confirmed egg eater is the Nile monitor, a big semiaquatic lizard that ranges almost all over Africa. Monitors are probably more frequently seen along the African rivers of today than any vertebrate except the birds. They live in burrows in the bank and often dive into the water ahead of an approaching boat. They eat the young crocodiles as well as the eggs. The same is true of the big African soft-shelled turtle. Although it lacks the enterprise to dig out crocodile eggs, it sometimes does so inadvertently during its own nesting activity.

Perhaps the most frequent source of friction in the life of grown-up crocodiles is the hippopotamus, with which both range and habitat are shared. Most of the time the two live together without strife, but at times hippos take great exception to the presence of crocodiles and drive them away. A female hippo, for example, methodically drives crocodiles away from the vicinity of her calf. There are records of large crocodiles being bitten completely in two by hippos. Crocodiles also sometimes get into difficulties when they annoy elephants at the water's edge. In his book *Sanctuary*, C. S. Stokes told of an unwise crocodile that seized the hind leg of a bathing elephant. The anguished trumpetings of the elephant stirred a companion to trample the crocodile, and the indignation of the elephant was quieted only when he had hoisted the crocodile from the water, found an appropriate tree on the shore and wedged the immense body firmly in a crotch high above the ground. It was no doubt an abnormally irascible elephant that did this, because crocodiles are rarely seen in trees. They are sometimes killed when they try to take prey away from the big carnivores, however, and there are even a few cases in which lions have been known to prey upon crocodiles.

Far from being a wholly baleful and disruptive influence in the natural world, the crocodile is a useful member of a complex ecosystem that can often be shown to have been damaged by the unnatural decline of crocodile numbers. While they are often thought to be relentless decimators of useful fish, the truth is their efforts are usually directed most strongly at predatory fish species, and the health of fishes as a whole is therefore best when crocodiles are around. Their comings and goings also help keep water channels open. They fertilize the water, giving increased productivity. Where they have been eliminated, there is often a great rise in the crab population, and since crabs do extensive damage to eggs and fry, this is also bad for the over-all fish population. As more is learned of the ecology of aquatic environments in Africa, the role of the crocodile is beginning, belatedly, to be seen as a necessary part of the natural organizations of which it is a member. Moreover, with proper management, based upon a program of careful research, the Nile crocodile could in some places be maintained as a stable source of valuable leather. Such management would not only stave off ruin for the reptile leather industry, which is rapidly committing suicide by immoderate mining of its raw materials, but would lessen the poaching pressure upon crocodiles in the national parks and in the waters of Africa generally.

As with all the other less-lovely beasts of the earth, however, the greatest significance of the old, gross crocodile is his role as a touchstone to test the hearts of men, to see if our kind will finally save crocodiles in some small spots here and there on the earth only because they were there before we came, and not for any other reason.

A FISHER OF SWAMPS AND STREAMS, THE CLAWLESS OTTER HAS ONLY TWO VESTIGIAL CLAWS GROWING ON ITS THIRD AND FOURTH HIND TOES

The Watery Wilds

The high plateaus of Africa cut away abruptly to low-lying rain forest and deep rift valleys—drained by immense rivers whose tributaries and reservoirs are refuges for crocodiles, hippos and peculiar assortments of fishes. In the east, pelicans wing in clouds from fresh-water lakes, flamingos mass in millions on an otherwise barren chain of salt lakes, and rare storks hide in the tall papyrus.

A NORTHWARD-WINDING TRIBUTARY, THE LOMAMI, PROVIDES SOME 250 OF THE 8,000 MILES OF NAVIGABLE RIVERS IN THE CONGO SYSTEM

The Great River Systems

Despite its enormous reaches of desert and dry savanna, Africa has its watery aspects. Three of the dozen largest lakes in the world lie within its boundaries, as do three of the dozen longest rivers; the Nile, in fact, at 4,132 miles, is *the* longest. The largest river in Africa from the point of view of volume, however, is the Congo, which pours more than a million cubic feet of muddy brown water into the Atlantic every second. It is the main drainage instrument for the West African rain forest and has dozens of major tributaries. By contrast, the Nile runs for much of its length through desert and has only three main streams. Many others are marked on the map as wadis, but more often than not they run only with sand. Both Nile and Congo have their sources in the clouds that hang perpetually over the Ruwenzori range. Their headwaters are actually only about 10 miles apart, but their mouths are separated by 5,754 miles of coastline.

The third great African river is the oddly flowing Niger. It starts in the granite hills of Temki Kundu, only about 150 miles from the western coast of Guinea, but runs east away from the sea, finally turning south in a tremendous curve and entering the Atlantic Ocean in Nigeria. It too is a rain forest river and contains more water than the Nile.

45

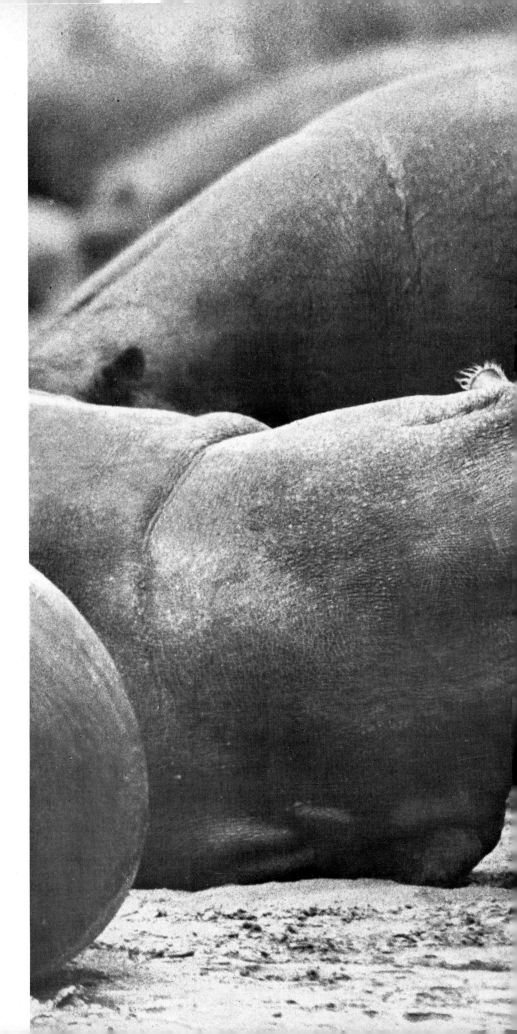

PHLEGMATIC HIPPOS bask on sand bars or loll in the water by day but grow more venturesome at dusk, wandering as far as 30 miles to graze along the shore. They are most abundant in the rivers and lakes of the western Rift Valley of Uganda; below Murchison Falls, thousands of them crowd in the calm pools of the Victoria Nile.

46

Water: Feast or Famine

In Africa, there is often too much water or not enough. Floods are common during the rainy seasons, and in places like the upper Zambezi their average rise is 40 feet above low water. This is made even worse by backwater from the Kariba Dam, which inundated thousands of miles of land in 1958. Lions fled the area. Buffaloes and elephants clustered on shrinking islands until hunger and rising water forced them to swim a mile or more to safe ground. Rhinos, which will not swim, had to be captured and removed by government rangers.

Between rains the land is apt to become parched. If the rains fail, as they sometimes do for a year or more, dreadful droughts ensue, aggravated by overgrazing by domestic cattle. The game gathers at the dwindling water holes. Elephants survive by digging for water in dried river bottoms. Rhinos and antelopes depend on the juices of drought-resistant plants, but in a long arid season the forage is eventually stripped bare and the animals begin to drop. The worst drought in 60 years hit East Africa in 1961, killing hundreds of thousands of animals.

A VICTIM OF FLOODING above the Kariba Dam, a soaked galago clings to floating vegetation. Snakes and monkeys climbed into treetops for safety, unaware that they were being engulfed by a man-made lake.

THE BONES OF A GIRAFFE bleach in the sun, as sandstorms rise over a dried lake bed in Amboseli, Kenya. Giraffes are able to browse treetops other animals cannot get to, but without water, many die.

THE CONGO UPSIDE-DOWN CATFISH, ONE OF SIX SPECIES IN AFRICA, SEEMS TO PREFER SWIMMING ON ITS BACK BUT USUALLY FEEDS RIGHT SIDE

THE ELECTRIC CATFISH, four feet long, lacks the sharp spines worn by most other catfish on the dorsal and pectoral fins but is far from defenseless—it discharges as much as 100 volts.

THE UBANGI MORMYRID, nine inches long, is a very small-mouthed fish which probes for worms and crustaceans in mud or sand with the single elongated barbel on its lower jaw.

UP, SWEEPING THE BOTTOM WITH THREE PAIRS OF SENSITIVE WHISKERS

FEATHERTAILS, three inches long, are among the myriad bite-sized species which teem in the warm fresh waters—a staple food of bigger fishes, and a popular tropical-fish export.

The Endemic Fishes

The lakes and rivers of Africa abound in endemic fishes adapted to nearly every fresh-water situation. Big predatory species range widely in the Zambezi, Congo and Nile Rivers, but many smaller ones have been partly or completely cut off from the mainstreams of fish life for millions of years. Near the Nile's source, above impassable Murchison Falls, predatory tiger fish and Nile perch are unknown, and in their absence an infinite variety of gemlike cichlids, only three or four inches long, has evolved in Lake Victoria, in practically no danger of being engulfed by an enormous mouth.

THE BUTTERFLY FISH, a miniature flying fish, sometimes skims the surface of the water, either gliding or flapping along on strong pectoral fins. Its maximum length is about five inches.

DISTICHODUS LUSSOSO, a rare, red-tailed Congo inhabitant, prized as an aquarium fish, may grow 16 inches long. Its flesh, an unappetizing yellow-orange, is nevertheless good to eat.

PELICANS ON LAKE NAIVASHA FLAP CLUMSILY UNTIL FULLY AIRBORNE BUT ARE STRONG FLIERS, OFTEN SOARING IN HUGE FLOCKS A THOUSAND FEET

The Waves of Water Birds

Although less varied than the fish life of Africa, the waterfowl—present in enormous numbers—are far more conspicuous. The great lakes of the Rift Valleys and the shallow basins occupied by Lake Victoria and Kioga are refuges for thousands of fishing and wading birds. In some areas they have become extremely shy because of shooting. But on more remote lakes, such as Rudolf and Edward, many kinds can still be seen feeding in their particular ways. The

THE MALACHITE KINGFISHER, only five inches long, is common on reedy lakes until, in the breeding season, it retires to the banks of a stream to dig its nesting tunnel.

OR MORE IN THE SKY. INVETERATE TRAVELERS, THEY SEEK A DISTANT ROOSTING PLACE AT NIGHT AND RETURN BEFORE DAWN THE NEXT DAY TO FISH

large white pelican uses its elastic throat pouch, together with its bill, as a net, and sometimes cooper-
ates with a dozen other individuals to drive small
fish into shallow water, where they can be more
easily surrounded and caught. Darters swim submerged, kingfishers hover and dive, ducks circle
close to the shore, and pink regiments of flamingos
scout the shallows or stand with heads upside down,
sifting the muddy water with their serrated bills.

THE SADDLE-BILLED STORK, one of the largest African
birds, stands about four feet tall. It hunts the marshes
like a heron—slowly stalking and then spearing its prey.

The Perils of a Too-salty Lake

Several of Africa's lakes are salty, and they are home to enormous flocks of flamingos that congregate to eat the microscopic creatures that grow in the alkali water and to build mud nests on the alkali flats. The biggest colonies—totaling about two million birds—normally live on Lake Natron in Tanganyika, but in 1962 floods inundated their nesting sites and forced them to move to another lake 30 miles away. Unfortunately this lake was saltier than Natron. As the hot, dry season progressed, its shores became a steaming broth of concentrated soda, and by late September 800,000 young birds were being encrusted with crystallized salts as quickly as they hatched and entered the water.

Ornithologists studying the new colony came to their rescue; in three weeks they managed to save 27,000 of the stricken chicks in certain lagoons where the soda concentration was the highest and prevent another 200,000 from entering the saturated areas. Then seasonal rains poured down, diluting the lake and ending the danger. But only half of the season's hatch lived to migrate back to Lake Natron.

BROKEN EGGS litter desolate, soda-saturated Lake Magadi after the exodus of flamingos. Late-nesting pairs abandoned eggs and young still in the mound nests to hyenas and vultures.

EXHAUSTED BY HEAVY ANKLETS of soda, a lesser flamingo chick lies in the mud. Rescuers broke the encrustations with hammers and kept the birds in pens until they could fly.

HUNTED FOR THEIR PLUMES, crowned cranes were nearly shot off the marshes, but under the protection of recent game laws are plentiful again, wandering in bands of three or more.

AN ODDITY OF THE PAPYRUS SWAMPS, the four-foot-tall shoe-bill stork rarely emerges from the floating islands, or sudd. It eats many small turtles, cracking their shells with its big bill.

Into the Jaws of Crocodiles

Master predator, cannibal and scavenger, the Nile crocodile has few peers among other animals. It can change its diet in a day from mammals to mollusks, it escapes dry seasons by digging itself deep into the mud below a river bed and takes full advantage of floods to extend its range far across inundated plains. When the water recedes, some individuals become trapped in small pools and may plod across dry land for miles on their short, bowed legs. For such bulky aquatic reptiles, they can move fast when necessary, sometimes sliding along on their bellies.

By constantly shifting from sun to shade on the

THE CROCODILE'S VICIOUS JAW IS ACTUALLY MORE OF A CLAMP THAN A BITING, SLASHING WEAPON. GETTING A FIRM GRIP ON A VICTIM, WITH

shore or basking partly submerged, the crocodile keeps its cold-blooded body within a six-degree range of its normal 78°F., coming closer than any other reptile to the efficient regulation of body heat which a warm-blooded animal enjoys. A strong swimmer and diver, it can submerge for an hour, about seven times longer than the hippo. None of these qualities, however, has helped the crocodile survive hunting by man. The toughest and the biggest individuals, up to 20 feet long, are gradually disappearing, and so are the large colonial nesting grounds, such as those still found on the south shore of Lake Albert.

POWERFUL TAIL STROKES THE CROCODILE ROLLS OVER AND OVER IN THE WATER UNTIL THE PREY DROWNS. THEN IT RIPS THE PREY UP AND EATS IT

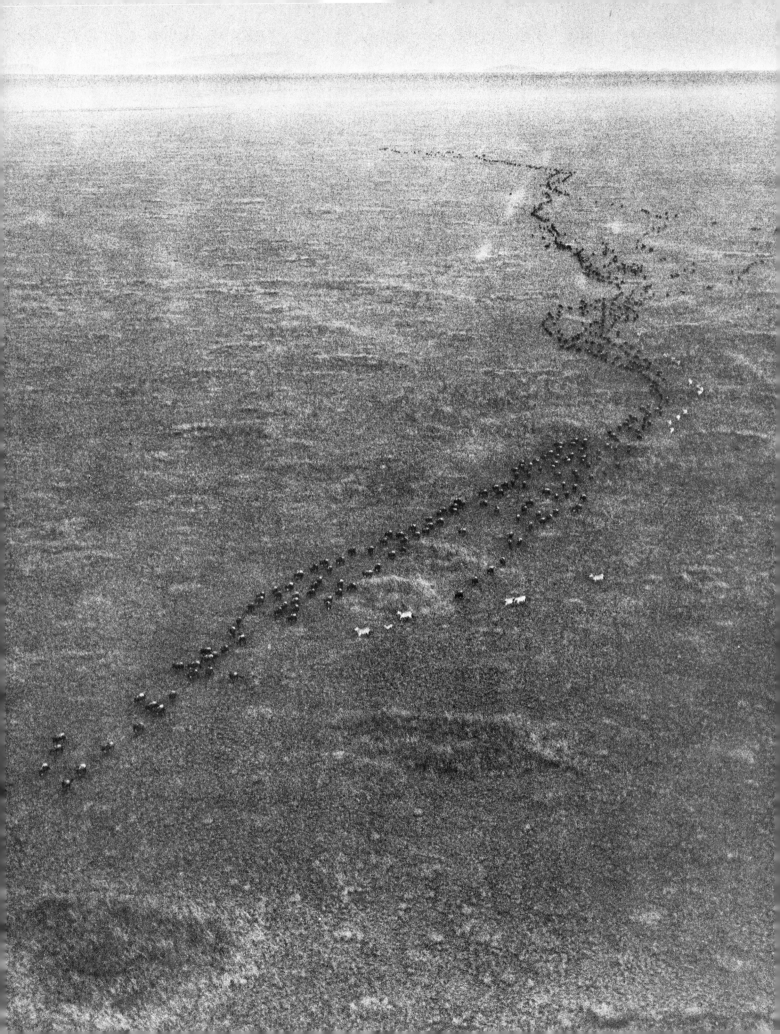

3

Grasslands and Great Game

IF there is one thing that nearly everybody knows about Africa it is that big animals live there. The beasts most likely to spring into the public mind when Africa is mentioned are elephants, zebras, rhinos, buffaloes, giraffes, a confusion of antelopes, and the lions, leopards and other kinds of predators that eat the eaters of leaves and grass. In the Swahili tongue this spectacular fauna is called *nyama*, which also is the word for meat. In English the fauna is usually referred to as game—the Big Game. That such a magnificent array of creatures should be named for its eating or sporting qualities seems natural to rural Africans who have always been a part of the game landscape. But it is a dismal misnomer, really. The big game of Africa is a great deal more than animals to be shot and meat to be eaten. It is an incomparable esthetic resource, too. It so happens that the meat-producing capacity of African savannalands is greater than that of any other natural area of the world; and, ironically, this may help save it in the changing times ahead. But its protein yield is not its real value to the human race. The savanna community of Africa is a priceless relic of the crest of the Age of Mammals.

This is no chance mixture of big animals thrown together on a plain. Like any natural grouping of live beings in any landscape—be it a millpond or a tract of Amazon rain forest—it is a biological community in which all sorts of mutual interaction takes place among the different kinds of plants and animals, and in which the activities of these modify the character of their living space. Both subjectively and scientifically the African big-game landscape is one of the most imposing ecological communities on earth.

African animals have been looked at so often in zoos that they seem to most people to belong there. Actually, each is, under natural conditions, a part of an organization. Knowledge of the existence of such organizations, of their subtlety and complexity, constitutes one of the important biological discoveries of recent times. This does not mean that each species on the plain must play a set role. Most of them are able to live in a series of different habitats, and some of the most ecologically versatile among them can range through great changes in environment. The important point is that these animals and plants do, to varying degrees, live together in the veld, and they all to some extent have evolved attributes that fit them for life in the community as a whole. While evolution is shaping a kind of animal for efficient grazing, for instance, it may also be smoothing off sharp edges that in a number of ways, both obvious and subtle, might disrupt the life and integrity of other sections of the community, impair the flow of energy through it and so redound to the disadvantage of all.

When gnus and ostriches occur in the same territory, they are often seen together, more intimately associated than chance could account for. This evidently is because the gnus gravitate to the ostriches in order to take advantage of them as a warning system. The ostrich is sharp-eyed, suspicious and seven or eight feet tall. Practically nothing can sneak up on an ostrich. So the gnus have through the ages fallen into the racial habit of edging up to ostriches. This is an example of ecological organization. That gnus manage to live pretty well when no ostriches are anywhere around simply shows that ecological ties can be advantageous without being obligatory.

T HE organization of the big-game landscape is not yet well understood. It is only in recent years that its accelerating depletion and threatened loss have stirred competent biologists to begin the painstaking studies that will be required to understand how it works. Some of the relationships within it are quite direct and evident. Nobody could fail to see the dependence of zebras on grass, for instance, or that of giraffes on trees with limbs of a proper height, or the need of lions for herbivores. The need of herbivores for lions, however—the dependence of grazers upon meat eaters to keep them from suicidal overpopulation and destruction of the range—is a less obvious sort of tie. And down in the soil the roles of small animals and plants in the complex series of conversion cycles of organic materials are almost completely unknown.

The habitat of the big game is tropical or subtropical grassland and savanna. This kind of country is the most abundant in Africa. It spreads west and east clear across the vast breadth of the continent from Senegal and Guinea to the Indian Ocean. It covers the plains of the Sudan and the high plateaus of the great lakes region, and it makes up the high veld and much of the low veld of South Africa. Savannas are a kind of landscape intermediate between steppe and forest. They develop where it rains hard for part of the year and little or not at all during another period of from three to eight months. This kind of climate favors the growth of grass, often by discouraging the growth of other plants. The grass may be all one kind or, more frequently, an association of several kinds.

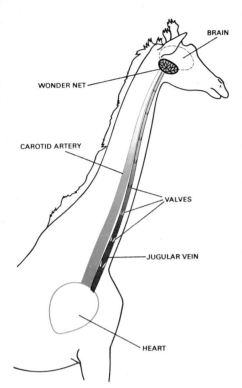

GETTING ENOUGH BLOOD TO THE GIRAFFE'S BRAIN

The giraffe has what may be the highest blood pressure in the world—and all because its neck is so long. For if the heart is to pump blood up the carotid artery to the brain, a distance of 10 to 12 feet, it must do so with enormous force. Not surprisingly, the heart is a massive affair two feet long with walls up to three inches thick, and weighing around 25 pounds. Blood leaves this powerful pump at a pressure two or three times that of a healthy man. By the time it reaches a spongy complex of small arteries, the so-called wonder net situated at the base of the brain, the pressure has been reduced (lighter color tone) by gravity and no damage can occur to the brain. The blood returns down the inch-wide jugular vein past a series of valves whose use is explained in the caption opposite.

There may be other herbaceous plants mixed in with the grass, and there are nearly always scattered trees. The trees are usually small-leafed and often are thorny. Some savannas are set with clumps of palms or of huge cactuslike euphorbias; or great pot-bellied baobab trees may be deployed singly about the plain, just as related pot-bellied trees are often spread over similar terrain in tropical America.

Among plant ecologists, there is a good deal of dissension over whether most of the savannas of the world, and especially those of the game regions of Africa, are really produced by climate. Nobody doubts that in some cases the rainfall regimen is the determining influence. The argument is over how much other factors—the pastoral pursuits and shifting agriculture of primitive man, the grazing of native ungulate herds, peculiarities of soil type and, above all, the effects of fire—have held the land in grass or grass-tree parklands that would change into something else if these factors were removed.

Anybody acquainted with the ecological principle of succession—the replacement of one kind of natural community by another in an orderly, predictable sequence of increasingly complex associations of animals and plants—will realize that the arguments over the African game landscape are really about whether or not it represents what is known as a climax community. In other words, is it the ultimate arrangement that can be reached under the current climatic and geologic conditions—an arrangement that would thenceforth remain stable if conditions remained stable? In the case of a rain forest or the Arctic tundra this question could be answered with some assurance. With savannas it can rarely be answered with any confidence at all. This kind of problem has great bearing on management and preservation practices in the African game country. Next to the problems brought on by growing African nationalism, it is the most harassing question on the continent today.

Even before modern man began his depredations upon the big game, it had begun to decline in diversity. The biological landscape of the African Pleistocene was more spectacular than that of the times of David Livingstone and Theodore Roosevelt. And the highest peak of savanna life was perhaps not reached in Africa at all, but on the plains of North America. The ice-age fauna of America lacked some of the fancy African creatures—the Old World rhinoceros for one—but it had mastodons and an array of other elephant kinds never equaled in the Old World for either ponderosity or multiplicity. There were in America herds of grazing camels and llamas, bison of great variety and size, horses of various kinds that ranged the plains in vast troops, and some elements missing entirely in Africa—for example, giant sloths, a whole constellation of species of pronghorns, armored glyptodons and herds of immense tortoises. This was the majestic brotherhood of the North American Pleistocene. When the ice ages with their great spreadings and dyings of animals had ended, a many-faced ungulate fauna was left only on the plains of Africa. Genetically speaking it is of course not the same fauna. There are no pronghorns in Africa, for example, and no native camels, and even the once-exuberant horses have dwindled to zebras and a few wild asses. But in spite of the epic depletion it has undergone, the Age of Mammals still clings to a little of its old grandeur in the African veld.

A key factor in the savanna landscape is periodic drought; the key life form there is grass. Many other plants and animals come and go through the savannas of the world, but grass is, in some degree of abundance and variety, common to them all. Grass is a monocotyledon—the more modern of the two great subdi-

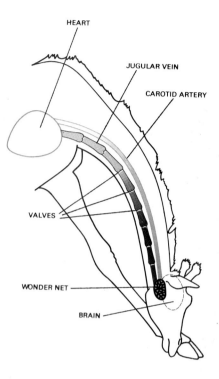

CONTROLLING THE PRESSURE IN THE GIRAFFE'S BRAIN

What happens when the giraffe bends down to drink? Why doesn't the rush of blood to the head burst vessels in the brain? And how does the blood get back to the heart? Apparently the following takes place: as blood flows into the wonder net, the many arteries in the net expand into the spaces between them. This temporarily reduces the pressure, just as water running from a small pipe into a larger one suffers a pressure drop, and protects the brain from damage. While the head is down, the valves in the jugular vein close, holding the blood in the neck and preventing it from running back into the head. As the pressure in the vein increases, it causes the pressure in the spaces of the net to rise also, counteracting the pressure being built up in the arteries by gravity—further guarding the brain from damage. Not until the giraffe straightens up does the excess blood flow into the heart through the open valves.

COPING WITH FIRE

Fire is a regular hazard in the savanna, and most grasses that grow there are able to grow again after a quick burning. Red oat grass survives because its seed is equipped to bury itself below a charred layer of soil (dark tone in drawings). The spiral tail, or awn, expands and contracts with heat and moisture, twisting the seed downward. The enlargements below show a single twist of the awn (right) and the bristles of the sharp tip (left), which anchor the seed and prevent it from backing up.

visions of flowering plants—and the dryland kinds of grasses are of fairly recent origin. One wonders whether there was any savannalike country in dinosaur days—any great expanses of open lands with dinosaurs cropping something other than grass. There may have been dry-season terrain in those days that looked superficially similar to veld. Little can be told from the record in the rocks. But for the plains landscape to reach its full expression—for communities like those of the African plateaus or the American Pleistocene to develop—there had to be grass or something very like it with another name.

So, it is not known exactly when grasslands in the modern sense spread in the world. There were grasses as far back as the Cretaceous, but they were evidently mainly tall, semiaquatic kinds that lived in swamps or in the shade of forest. Although the fossil record of dryland grasses—the kinds upon which all modern savannalands are founded—is sketchy, grass had such a strong influence on the evolution of some lines of mammals that one can trace its spread by the changes in fossil bones and teeth of horses, pronghorns and cattle. The first known bunch grass is from the Lower Miocene, about 25 million years ago. It was at this time that horses began to show rudiments of their modern skeletal traits, and only a little later a brand-new ungulate family, the Bovidae, appeared. This group was based upon a different but obviously equivalent set of evolutionary changes in teeth, feet and build. It eventually branched into various kinds of cattle, sheep, goats and antelopes. So grass has been a potent factor in mammal history—just as it has in human history. Much can be told about the grasslands of the past by studying remains of the animals that lived in them.

THE features of this fated vegetable, grass, which directly or indirectly account for its importance to mammals are a high nutritional value and a marked resistance to drought, to grazing damage and to fire. Or, put another way, it is mainly the ability of grass to avail itself quickly of heavy rainfall after prolonged drought and physical damage. These are the traits that qualify grass as a prime producer of savanna country and as a molder of mammal lives and lines. A grass plant has a fibrous root mass, which holds well in dry-season soil. When killed down by drought or fire, or when grazed down by the teeth of animals, the plant rapidly grows up again from ground level. This is not possible among most plants, whose zones of growth are at the tips of leaves, shoots or roots. A grass grows at the base of its leaf, and close cropping by animal teeth does not affect its ability to keep growing. Grasses are mostly wind pollinated and are also adept at asexual reproduction by putting out long rodlike runners. This makes them independent of insects, which is a good thing, because many insects are unable to put up with the dry conditions of the plains habitat. The leaves of grass fight drought by curling lengthwise into troughs or tubes. This cuts down the surface exposed to evaporation and keeps the blade from collapsing when it wilts. Further mechanical strength is furnished by silica deposited in the walls of the cells. This latter adaptation not only helps keep the grass stiff when it loses its turgor but it also helps build horses and antelopes. It is but one of the factors, all stemming basically from the drought of the savanna dry season, that can be traced through millions of years of time merely by looking at changes in the structure of hoofed animals.

The most noticeable features of ungulate mammals are large size, long legs and high-crowned teeth with finely ridged grinding surfaces. The silica in the grass makes it abrasive and hard on teeth. And because grass will stand close cropping, animals bite it off close to the earth, picking up sand and doing more damage to their teeth. A result of ages of such abrasive chewing has been the development of the extraordinary molar tooth of the grazing ungulate, which by one path in horses and another in the bovids has reached a common condition. In both it is a long tooth with short roots, high crown and a surface in which vertical layers of glass-hard enamel alternate with softer dentyne. The materials wear away at different rates, and this keeps the surface finely ridged for more chewing of more abrasive grass. The teeth of many grazers have open roots, which enable them to keep growing to compensate for surface wear.

LIKE the teeth of the ungulates, the fewness of their toes is directly related to the open, dry environment too. The loss of toes in both the odd-toed kinds, such as the horse and rhinoceros, and the even-toed pronghorns and cattle is fundamentally an adaptation to wide-open spaces. Running fast is most useful where the ground is dry and hard, and where there are no obstructions to dodge among or hide behind. It can be done best there if the runner has a relatively small, hard, dry foot. Both the one-toed horse foot and the cloven hoof of the gazelle are beautifully made for the purpose. One reason big herbivores in open country must run is to get away from predators. Another is the same factor that made the landscape to start with—the dry season. An alternating of dry and wet periods makes travel necessary if one is to stay near grass and water. So we begin to see the climate molding not just the landscape but teeth and feet too, with grass serving as a direct agent of the change in the teeth and an indirect influence in the case of the hoofs.

The generally big size of ungulates likewise is an adaptation directly and indirectly related to the savanna habitat. Other things being equal, a big animal runs faster and can travel farther than a little one. Moreover, as the size of an animal increases, there is a disproportionate increase in the area of grinding surface of the teeth. If the creature is a browser, reach also becomes an important factor favoring increased size. Big animals make more efficient use of the food they eat. The cud-chewing plant eaters require storage and fermentation chambers in their digestive tubes, and these no doubt impose space requirements that a mouse would find hard to meet. So savanna animals tend to be big, and because they walk on the grass, grasses not able to put up with being

COPING WITH GRAZERS

On the East African savanna the favorite food of many of the herbivores is Bermuda, or saw-toothed, grass. This hardy ground cover, often only five or six inches tall, actually prospers on close cropping. The grazing animal eats all but the bottom leaves lying flat on the ground. These are adequate to sustain the plant while it rapidly grows up again. The runners which produce new seed-bearing stems also lie flat on the ground or under the surface, and are equally safe from the grazer's teeth.

trodden upon gave up the ghost long ago. Thus causes and effects get thoroughly mixed, and even when one confines one's prying to the interactions between a single plant—grass—and the hoofed animals, the ramifications get quickly beyond all accounting. But when one mows one's lawn with confidence that it will grow right back again, it should come to mind that this is partly because of the feet and teeth of long-dead ungulates.

A SHOW OF HOOFS

ANOTHER potent factor involved in many ways in the organization of the savanna landscape is fire. Although the detailed effects of fire are poorly known, no one doubts that the veld burns from time to time, by natural or human agency, and that it always has—and that every kind of living thing in the savanna landscape has evolved built-in adjustments to the disaster and blessing of fire. When a grass fire runs before the wind, there are two things a being made of protoplasm can do. It can run too or it can hide in the ground. The grass hides in the ground, as the wart hogs do, along with the mole rats, worms and bacteria. At least, it hides its necessary parts. To grass, a fire is no worse a calamity than drought, or than being heavily grazed or heavily trodden. Too-frequent fires can ruin a landscape, but a single fierce fire leaves grass alive in the earth. And it also leaves alive any big, fast animal which, because of fires, or of the need to run from predators or to migrate long distances after food or water, has evolved the capacity for fast, far travel. So here again a factor—fire in this case—works both directly and through the agency of go-between grass to shape ungulates.

I have so far spoken mainly of the African savanna animals collectively as an ecological community. This has to be dwelt upon a bit, because the usual person seeing a giraffe is so taken with the beast itself that no thought is left for its history or ecology. I have only barely hinted at some of the kinds of relationships that built the savanna landscape. With the present state of knowledge of savanna ecology, no adequate description of this fantastic community would be possible, even if there were space here to give it. But something should be said of the pure prodigal diversity of the hoofed animals of the veld.

As in any natural ecological association, some animals—and the same holds for the plants—are restricted to the veld, while others range widely through a great spread of varied living space. Of wide-ranging creatures the elephant is the supreme example, next to man probably the most versatile of all occupants of the habitats of the earth. Nevertheless, elephants are deeply involved in the savanna organization. Their role is not just the harvesting of grass and leaves. They make an important contribution in maintaining the environment by their slapdash, powerful browsing, and pruning and trail-cutting habits. In some kinds of country, the dropping out of the elephant element would result in drastic changes in vegetation and thus in the fauna as a whole. The elephants of today—the African *Loxodonta* and Indian *Elephas*—are a remnant of a much more diverse array of Pliocene and Pleistocene kinds. They are the close kin of the mammoths of the ice ages and less nearly related to the mastodons, which were a somewhat more primitive group.

One of the more subtle ways in which African antelopes differ from each other is in the size and shape of their hoofs. The gerenuk (above), living in dry, scrubby areas of Somalia and Kenya, feeds on the leaves of Acacia trees and must often stand upright to browse. Its pointed, triangular hoofs help brace it. The sassaby (below), of East and South African grasslands, is Africa's fastest antelope. Smooth and untiring in its stride, the sassaby is given sure footing in soft or sandy soil by its big hoofs.

At the other end of the scale of ungulate size are the little hyraxes—dassies, or conies—related to the elephants but ecologically more comparable to rabbits. Hyraxes are stout-bodied, tailless little animals with short toes, four on the front foot and three on the hind foot. There are a great many kinds of hyraxes, some living in trees, some among rocks. They are said to be the only animals able to stare at the sun.

Of the perissodactyls—the odd-toed hoofed animals—only the zebras, the rhinoceros and, in the extremely dry northern sections, the wild ass have held on in Africa today. Zebras are still widespread and make up a conspicuous part of most mixed game herds. The black rhino is less gregarious and less often seen. Its food is mostly twigs and leaves. Like the elephant, its browsing and the ground-conditioning influences of its trampling are important factors in the organization of many African game communities. The nearly extinct white rhinoceros is mainly a grazer.

The pig family is represented by the nocturnal bush pig and the somewhat bigger wart hog, which lives in burrows in the earth. The closely related hippopotamus spends most of its time in the water but often wanders far out onto the plains to graze.

What the horses and pronghorns were on the American ice-age plains, the cattle family has become in Africa. The Bovidae is the biggest of hoofed-animal families, with some 50 genera, and is the most recent of all mammal families to evolve. Its members are cloven-hoofed and in all of them unbranched permanent horns are borne by one or both sexes. The horns are made of a hollow sheath of hard material molded over a core of bone. Besides the various kinds of cattle, buffalo and bison, the group includes goats and sheep, and antelopes. The most cowlike of the wild bovids of Africa is the buffalo, a massive animal that may stand five feet high at the shoulder and weigh as much as a ton. The African buffalo has spectacular horns with ponderous broad bases and an outside spread of nearly five feet.

B<small>Y</small> far the most populous and diverse element in the African savanna fauna is the antelope family. These are not the creatures known as antelopes on the plains of the western United States. Those have two-branched horns and are properly called pronghorns. They belong to a different family, intermediate between cattle and deer, and, like them, have evolved long-crowned molar teeth for grazing. There used to be a great number of different kinds of pronghorns in the Pliocene, but they have always been restricted to America, and now only one species remains.

African antelopes range in shoulder height from 10 inches to almost six feet and reach weights of over 1,500 pounds. All antelopes have horns in at least one sex. Some are straight, some twisted in tight corkscrews, some in open spirals, some are backswept like sickles, some outcurved into lyrelike figures, some bent into unaccountable compound curves. Some horns are little more than bumps on the head of the bearer, some are 60 inches long and more. In some kinds the female has no horns, in others she has longer ones than the male.

The South African klipspringer (above), a small antelope of rocky regions, has rounded hoofs which give it a tiptoe look. It springs off the ground, and with all four feet held together can land on a pinnacle no bigger than a silver dollar. The sitatunga (below), one of the world's few aquatic antelopes, lives in swampy areas of Central and West Africa and takes refuge in the water. Its banana-shaped hoofs, seven and a half inches long, prevent it from sinking in the mud but make it an awkward runner.

Although African antelopes are pre-eminently animals of brush or open country and evidently have been from their beginnings, they have undergone all sorts of secondary branching and have moved into widely divergent habitats and ways of life. The savanna landscape is never a homogeneous spread of grass and scattered trees. It abuts upon or is broken by cliffs and hills. It is cut by ravines or by streams which may be permanent or sporadic. It is rimmed with broad flood plain or with gallery forest. Even the flat savanna itself, the open landscape with scattered trees and with grass in between, may vary markedly in the kinds and quantity of food it offers and in the water ration it doles out. It is into this system of intergrading landscapes that the African antelope fauna has radiated—whether through evolution in place or by moving into it from elsewhere will take the paleontologist more time to tell—and the result is one of the most imposing examples of the partitioning of a living space by big, warm-blooded vertebrates that can be found anywhere in the world.

This exciting array of horned ruminants has been classified by mammalogists in a number of separate subfamilies. If this had been done on purely esthetic grounds, the result no doubt would have been a group of graceful, handsome antelopes on the one hand and a group of odd-looking-to-grotesque kinds on the other. The latter would be the tribe of the hartebeests and wildebeests. Of the two, the wildebeest, or gnu, is the uglier by far; but none of these species are as esthetically pleasing in appearance as antelopes are supposed to be. The trouble with them is their elongated, narrow muzzles, the peculiar shapes and mounting of their horns, the steep slope of the back from the shoulders to the rump, and the lumbering look this gives their gait when they run. Actually both wildebeest and hartebeest cover ground at a good clip when in a hurry, but they seem to make oddly heavy going of it. There are two kinds of wildebeest, one of them now almost extinct, and several species of hartebeest. The common ones are often conspicuous in the herds of the East African plateau plains. The bastard hartebeests, including the topi and sassaby, have a good deal more antelope grace than the other members of the group.

Another tribe is that of the bushbucks, the kudus, the sitatungas, the rare nyalas, and the elands, good-sized to huge animals with short muzzles and twisted horns. The kudus are perhaps the most sought-after of all the antelopes by trophy hunters. A big male is without any doubt one of the most strikingly statuesque of all vertebrate animals. The giant eland is the biggest antelope. It stands nearly six feet at the shoulder and looks more like an ox than like the usual antelope. The weight of a full-grown male may go as high as a ton. In spite of its huge size this eland is an extraordinary jumper. The members of a herd sometimes jump over each other's backs when alarmed. If it were not for this incongruous talent, which makes it hard to fence in elands, they probably would have been domesticated long ago, because the meat, milk and hide are all excellent. In fact, experimental eland husbandry has been going on for years in both Rhodesia and the Ukraine. In both places the animal has proved wholly amenable to being kept as a meat and dairy animal.

The sable, roan and oryx antelopes make up another group. They are all big, coarse-haired animals with short muzzles and ringed horns. Oryxes are able to live without free water, deriving it wholly from their food. Baby oryxes are among the only ruminants that have horns at birth.

THE gazelles and their kind are the epitome of antelope grace and speed. In Kenya and Tanganyika most mixed herds of antelopes include either Thomson's or Grant's gazelle, or both. The superb springbok is the only South African gazelle. The impala, although a little bigger than the true gazelles, is comparably athletic. It jumps with a suddenness and seeming lack of effort that suggest the dramatic muscular feats of fishes and porpoises.

Another group of antelopes includes the reedbucks and waterbucks. The group as a whole shows a strong attachment to marsh and water. The common waterbuck is one of the most widespread and numerous of African antelopes. The kob and the puku are short-grass grazers that go and come between stream borders, swamps and savannas. The lechwes also belong to this group and are among the most aquatic of all the antelopes. They have long, narrow hoofs and are strong swimmers. Often found feeding on water plants, belly deep in the water, they are sometimes even seen sleeping in shallow water. Among the most

THE IMPALA'S FLAG

At a distance and viewed from the side, the impala has a tawny appearance that hides its outline from lions, leopards and cheetahs—all of which hunt by sight. However, it is strikingly marked on the rear with a black-and-white flag that is most conspicuous when the animal is leaping or running. At a warning snort from a sentinel guarding the herd, each impala bounds off, flashing black stripes on its tail and hindquarters, and black spots on its heels, indicating the direction of escape to the others behind it and so keeping the herd together.

diminutive of all hoofed animals are the dik-diks, little antelopes about the size of a fox terrier, with spiked horns and a tuft of hair on the top of the head. There are about a dozen species in Africa, most of them in East Africa.

The most primitive of the antelopes are the duikers, small- to medium-sized animals found mainly in forest, but also represented in savanna and bush country. The name duiker means "diver" in Afrikaans and refers to the way the creature plunges into the bush when startled.

In thinking of the savanna as an integrated community, one should not get the notion that its boundaries are rigidly set and the animals and plants in it all wholly committed to special inflexible roles. Actually, there is a great deal of interchange between the different communities of any landscape, and the African veld is no exception. Some of the plains antelopes may pass their whole lives within the heart of one fairly homogeneous tract of country, moving only enough to keep themselves within good patches of browse or grass, or within reach of a water hole if they are of kinds that must have water. But consider the relationships of such species as the klipspringer and the lechwe to the plains community. Both are antelopes, and both at times mix with the more generalized harvesters of the savanna vegetation. But for most of their lives the two are well out of the mainstream of the savanna ecosystem—the klipspringer scrambling like a lizard about the cliffs and walls of rocky ravines in search of the sere harvest there, the lechwe sopping about the wet edges of the plain where it grades into marsh.

ANOTHER aspect of the plains community that keeps one from thinking of it as a closed system is the migrations of its members. Partly the migratory habit is simply an outcome of seasonal changes in the landscape; partly it is a result of the strong tendency of savanna herbivores to gang together and so to make great demands on the forage in any given place. Migrations of the savanna fauna can be either regular or sporadic, and they range in extent from the tremendous journeys undertaken by elephants to minor shifts between seasonally changing sections of the habitat. Spectacular periodic migrations of wildebeests occur in the Serengeti in Tanganyika, and nearly all the plains antelopes are forced to make scheduled shifts in territory, by changes in forage or water resources, or by special needs during the period of reproduction.

One antelope, the South African springbok, makes—or used to make—sporadic catastrophic journeys, perhaps the most stupendous mass movements of any terrestrial mammal. The causes of these great hegiras have never been satisfactorily explained, and it is now too late to do more than speculate about them, although many were still taking place at the end of the last century.

Between 1887 and 1896, there were four great springbok treks in the Prieska District of the Karoo in Cape Province. These were witnessed by a local citizen, T. B. Davie, who wrote of them thus:

". . . When the trek was in full move nothing but springbok were to be seen for miles upon miles at a stretch. The whole country seemed to move, not in any hurry or rush, as is generally associated in people's minds with a springbok, but a steady plodding walk march, just like 'voetganger' (hopper) locusts; no other animal or insect life can afford so apt an illustration. The writer has seen them in one continuous stream, on the road and on both sides of the road, to the sky-line, from the town of Prieska to Draghoender, a distance of 47 miles, plodding on, just moving aside far enough to avoid the wheels of the cart.

"On this occasion the owners of the farm Witvlei were all sitting in a ring

THE PRONKING SPRINGBOK

Another spectacular signal on the open veld is the "pronking" of the springbok. When excited or alarmed, this graceful antelope leaps into the air, with head lowered, back arched and feet together. This pulls erect a conspicuous row of white hairs which ordinarily lie out of sight on its back. Again and again the springbok pronks, informing other individuals of danger before they all race away, crests now flattened and partly covered by dark fur. The young bucks begin to practice this maneuver in play when they are a few days old.

round the top of the well, which at that time was uncovered, the father, son and son-in-law armed with rifles, firing a shot now and then, and the women folk with sticks and stones trying to keep the 'boks' away. This was the family's only water supply left, as the 'boks' had already filled up the dam, thousands being trampled to death in the mud as they pressed on over one another to get to the water. At last the 'boks' beat the farmers and got to the well and in a few minutes it was full of dead and dying 'boks.' However, the trek passed before evening with the exception of a few stragglers and the Witvlei people soon had their well cleaned out and rendered serviceable. . . . In the course of a few days the trek seems to melt away. They disappear, nobody knows where they have gone to. . . ."

In 1888 Davie and a Dr. Gibbons, a naturalist, tried to estimate the number of springbok in a trekking herd:

"In the morning as soon as it was daylight we were out, and there we were sure enough in a veritable sea of antelopes. The Doctor saw at once, upon being rallied as to counting them, that it was impossible, but he made a guess after this fashion. Seeing a kraal (a fold for stock) a good large one, he asked how many sheep could stand in it, and Mr. Danth replied 1,500. 'Well,' said the Doctor, 'if 1,500 can stand there, then about 10,000 can stand on an acre, and I can see in front of me 10,000 acres covered with "boks"; that means at least 100,000,000; then what about the miles upon miles around on all sides as far as the eye can reach covered with them?' He gave it up. We left Nels Poortje after breakfast and rode for $4\frac{1}{2}$ hours right straight through them, they never giving more road than was required for us to pass . . ."

The springboks were said to travel about a hundred miles in a day. According to C. S. Stokes, the moving avalanche often caught up domestic stock, carried it along until calves and sheep among them were exhausted and trampled to death. He tells of two African shepherd boys who were killed the same way, and of a lion that was "borne onward by the overwhelming waves of the gazelles." Sometimes the treks kept moving westward until they reached the sea. One such suicidal climax occurred on the Namaqualand coast near the mouth of the Orange River. According to a witness, when this had spent itself, millions of the springboks had died, and their bodies formed a wall that extended for more than 30 miles along the coast.

If the factors bringing about these vast journeyings could be known, they would surely shed light upon hidden and fundamental problems of population dynamics and community ecology. But the last of the great treks occurred during the 1890s. After that the terrific hunting pressure, combined with outbreaks of rinderpest, reduced the springbok populations to the small herds of today. These stay pretty much in one place.

In this quick sketch of the savanna fauna I have mentioned only an arbitrary few of its features. Nothing has been said, for instance, of the spectrum of carnivorous animals that preys upon the ruminants. They will come up in another chapter. The small mammals down in the grass, up in the trees and in burrows under the ground have been ignored too, and so have the birds and reptiles of the veld. Some of these are told of in other parts of the book. The invertebrates of the soil have been slighted, although their part in the veld community is probably as vital as that of all the big animals on top of the ground put together. Almost nothing will be said about them anywhere in the book, because almost nothing is known.

THE UGANDA KOB relishes tender, marshy grasses and seldom strays more than 400 yards from water. Like other plains antelopes, it has suffered from man's depletion of its habitat, and unrestricted hunting.

The Array of Herbivores

Lacking in rich soils, the African plateau is only fertile and productive when utilized by a wide variety of wild herbivores with diversified feeding habits. Elephants, rhinos and more than 60 kinds of antelopes are among those that graze or browse the riverine, mountain and valley forests, the dry bush and the open savanna. Even the elephant's wholesale uprooting of trees is a helpful plowing that aerates ground otherwise undisturbed for centuries.

DAWN ON THE EAST AFRICAN SAVANNA SILHOUETTES GRAZING THOMSON'S GAZELLES AND UMBRELLA-SHAPED ACACIA TREES. WIDELY SCATTERED

The Hordes on the Plains

More large herbivores are concentrated on the savannas and dry bush of East Africa than on any comparable area in the world. On the Serengeti-Mara Plains, the density may be as high as 100 animals per square mile. This kind of "crowding" is only possible because each species has a year-round diet which rarely conflicts with the others. Giraffes feed mostly on trees, black rhinos on brush, and wildebeests on grass. There are preferences for certain grasses, but these are eaten at different stages of growth. Wildebeests crop red oat grass until it is about four inches high, zebras when it is mature, and topis when it has dried. The majority of the plains animals are migratory and constantly seek places where rainfall, fire or perhaps grazing have produced grass of the preferred height and consistency. The distances covered in these travels may be over 1,000 miles each year. Resident species, such as impala and dik dik, change from grass to browse as these are seasonally available on the home range.

IN SMALL GROUPS, THESE ANTELOPES FAR OUTNUMBER THE PLAINS WILDEBEESTS, WHICH ARE CONCENTRATED AT TIMES IN TENS OF THOUSANDS

UNDER A PROTECTIVE CANOPY of thorn bushes, impalas are shaded and concealed. They prefer to feed along forest edges, but in recent years the bush country of East Africa has been increasingly broken up into farms, forcing them into the open.

Pressure from Within and Without

Since the African herbivores have many predators, much of their energy is spent in guarding against attacks. Shy as they appear, however, these animals are highly aggressive within their own social structures. In rutting season—a few weeks every year—bull sables snort and scrape the ground, challenging each other to battles over two or three square miles of bush and a few cows. A stretch of open plain occupied by a big herd of wildebeests is also broken up into a mosaic of territories with bulls circling them and frequently butting trespassers. At calving time, pressures from the outside are most crucial, especially on the plain, where the newborn must be quicker to gain their feet than young in the bush. On Serengeti, each year enough wildebeest calves survive to keep the population at about 200,000—in close balance with approximately 700 lions.

A TERRITORIAL BATTLE between giant sables begins with sparring (*top, left*), but the challenger soon desists and is chased away (*center and bottom*). Ebony-coated and magnificently horned, the sable is one of the most elegant antelopes —and perhaps the rarest. About 700 inhabit dense bush in Angola.

A NEWBORN WILDEBEEST lies in the grass for no more than five minutes (*top, right*) before it stands up and runs to its mother (*center*). Its ability to follow her closely and keep up with the moving herd is of great survival value on the plains, where a hungry predator is always waiting to grab a lost calf (*bottom*).

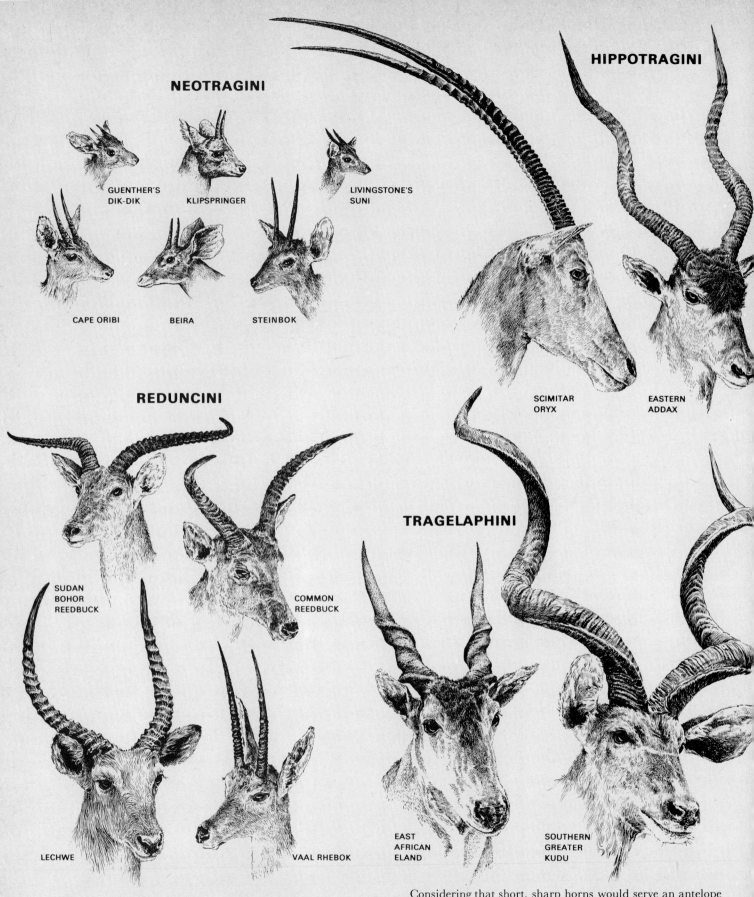

NEOTRAGINI

GUENTHER'S
DIK-DIK

KLIPSPRINGER

LIVINGSTONE'S
SUNI

CAPE ORIBI

BEIRA

STEINBOK

HIPPOTRAGINI

SCIMITAR
ORYX

EASTERN
ADDAX

REDUNCINI

SUDAN
BOHOR
REEDBUCK

COMMON
REEDBUCK

LECHWE

VAAL RHEBOK

TRAGELAPHINI

EAST
AFRICAN
ELAND

SOUTHERN
GREATER
KUDU

MULTIPLE SOLUTION
OF A SINGLE PROBLEM

Considering that short, sharp horns would serve an antelope well enough in combats between males or as defensive weapons against predators, it is remarkable that so many different kinds have evolved. Here, in a gallery of heads representing the seven tribes and 24 genera of African antelopes, are a

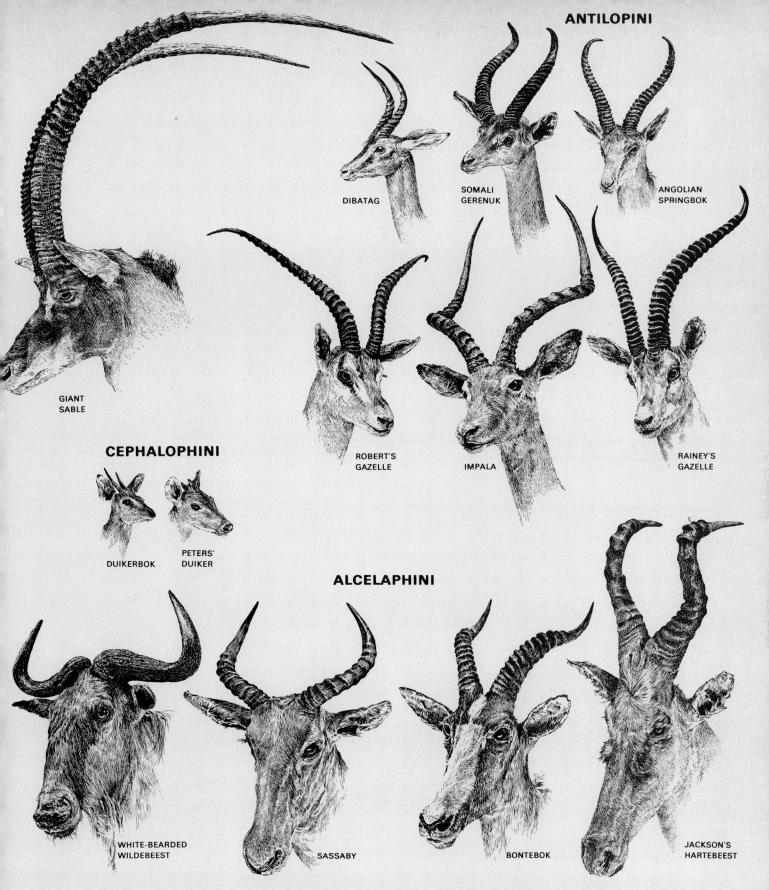

ANTILOPINI

DIBATAG

SOMALI GERENUK

ANGOLIAN SPRINGBOK

GIANT SABLE

CEPHALOPHINI

DUIKERBOK

PETERS' DUIKER

ROBERT'S GAZELLE

IMPALA

RAINEY'S GAZELLE

ALCELAPHINI

WHITE-BEARDED WILDEBEEST

SASSABY

BONTEBOK

JACKSON'S HARTEBEEST

variety of solutions to a single problem—the shape of a horn. The reasons for the diversity are obscure. Why, for example, are the reedbuck's horns forward-curling or the springbok's lyre-shaped with inward-facing points, or the impala's twisted? How about the duiker's, which are small in proportion to its body, or those of the giant sable, which seem needlessly long and heavy? Probably none is perfectly engineered, but all serve their purposes. The sable, for example, wields its rapier-sharp horns very efficiently. With quick turns of its head, it can impale as large and formidable an enemy as a leopard.

77

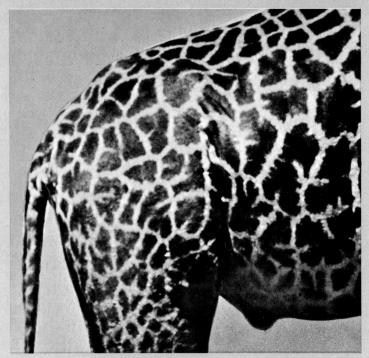

THE COMMON GIRAFFE has a mosaic of spots which are paler and less noticeable in the young but grow darker with age.

THE RETICULATED GIRAFFE is more conspicuous in the open than the common giraffe but difficult to see in trees or brush.

THOMSON'S GAZELLE, a plains animal, has a disruptive black band on its side that helps break up the shape of its body.

THE BUSHBUCK, found in open thorn forest, wears a coat of barrel-hoop stripes and spots resembling shafts of soft sunlight.

The Confusing Camouflage of the Hunted

The living place, habits, means of defense and enemies of the hunted animal are all reflected in its skin pattern, and in Africa there are endless variations. The antelopes of the forest and bush rest motionless by day and have spots and stripes that blend with the surroundings. If alarmed while feed-

BURCHELL'S ZEBRA, the common plains variety, shows stripes that are conspicuous by day but help conceal it at twilight.

GREVY'S ZEBRA, found in the northern bush, is more finely striped than other zebras; at a distance it appears solid gray.

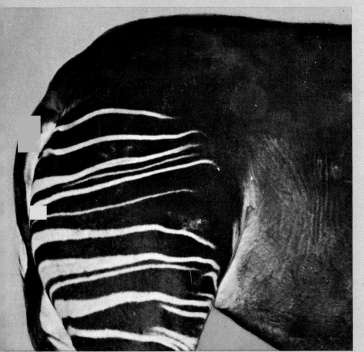

THE OKAPI of the Congo blends into the forest; markings on its flanks and legs simulate streaks of sun piercing the canopy.

THE BONGO, a dweller in high mountain forests of East Africa, is well hidden by its stripes while feeding in stands of bamboo.

ing or drinking, their first reaction is to freeze in order to remain unnoticed. By contrast, the animals of the plains, which depend less on coloration than speed for survival, have bold disruptive markings which tend to disguise their shapes but are seldom concealing. In the full sunlight of open country, the zebra's pattern is dazzling, and because of this conspicuousness, zebras are far more nervous and active than their habitual associates on the plains, the wildebeests. At dusk, however, when lions—their chief predators—are most likely to attack, zebras become almost invisible, especially in thin cover.

79

The Ill-tempered Titans

As long as it had only other animals to deal with, the rhinoceros did well. Great bulk, an inch-thick hide, a sharp horn on its nose and a willingness to charge have ensured over the eons that this tanklike creature be unmolested in its daily routine. These characteristics do not guarantee protection against man, however, and today rhinos are disappearing. Africa has two kinds. The bigger and gentler, the

THE WHITE RHINO, the second largest land mammal, is not white but dark gray. Its name—derived from the Boer *wyt*, or wide—refers to a broad, square jaw adapted to grazing.

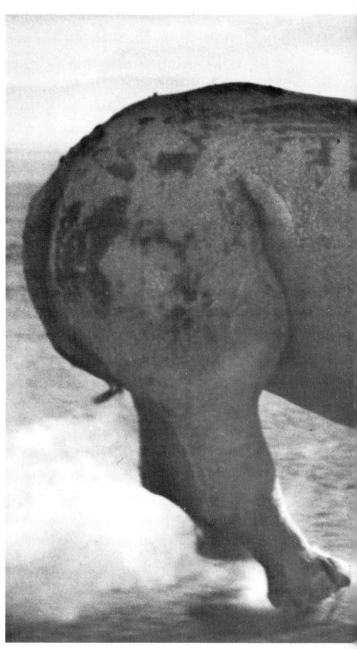

THE BLACK RHINO has a narrower face with a prehensile upper lip for eating leaves. It too is gray, but both animals often look very light in color from wallowing in the mud or dust.

CHARGING ON THE AMBOSELI PLAIN, a black rhino reaches 30 miles per hour. For its bulk, the rhinoceros is extremely agile. It takes off like a sprinter and turns like a polo pony.

so-called white rhino, is a grass eater of the plains, now nearing extinction; only about 2,000 live in South and Central Africa. Its more common and peppery relative, the black rhino, is a browser usually found in dry, brushy country, where it delicately nibbles leaves from shrubs and trees. Black rhinos may still be seen in most of the game parks of East Africa, but elsewhere they are almost gone.

Rhinos operate under numerous handicaps in modern Africa. They have a very low reproductive rate —one calf about every three years. They do not readily adapt to changed diet or living conditions. Their solitary habits do not give them the herd protection that many other herbivores enjoy. Finally, their horns are prized for their medicinal qualities, and they are heavily poached by natives.

It is an odd mixture of short temper and curiosity. These traits, plus poor eyesight, have encouraged the habit of charging first and investigating later, and, curiously, have served it well against such hereditary enemies as the Wakamba tribesmen, who hunt it with arrows. When chased into the thorn bush by a rhino, the hunters cannot use their bows effectively.

IN SINGLE FILE, elephants trek through Tsavo Park. They have a pace of five miles per hour, covering 20 or 30 miles a day in their journeys to and from water. When the water holes dry up, herds gather along the rivers.

ENJOYING A DUST BATH without getting off its feet, an elephant first sucks the dirt into its hose-like trunk and then blows it over its entire body.

Too Many Elephants?

The biggest quadrupeds on earth, African elephants have exerted a tremendous influence on their living places—opening up the forest for bush animals, and the denser bush to plains dwellers like the oryx and wildebeest. An elephant may weigh up to seven tons and requires more than a sixth of a ton of vegetation per day. This means that it must graze and browse for at least 16 hours out of every 24. It often wanders long distances in search of tender leaves and tempting fruits—and if these are out of reach, will shake or up-root trees to obtain them.

As long as elephants ranged freely, their activities were no more harmful than lightly combing fires. Now they gather in protected areas, such as South Africa's Kruger and Kenya's Tsavo Park, which are too arid to support large populations. In the last several years, about 10,000 elephants in Tsavo's eastern section have completely destroyed the range—not only for themselves but for other animals as well—for 15 miles around the few rivers that run during the dry season.

A FELLED BAOBAB is nibbled by a youngster. During long periods of drought, elephants not only eat the leaves and bark but also chew up soft, woody baobab fibers to extract the juices.

UP TO ITS TUSKS, an elephant lazes in the Victoria Nile River of Murchison Falls Park. Where rainfall and forage permit, herds may stay close to permanent water throughout the year.

THE FAMILY GROUP, composed of from five to 15 "relatives"— cows, calves and perhaps one or two young bulls—is the basic unit of elephant society. In Africa, as many as 200 may band together at various times of the year, but the old bulls prefer to go off by themselves, leaving small maternally ruled herds, like the one shown here, in which the cows supervise family raising. These groups can be distinguished from bachelor parties, even at a distance, by the trumpeting of the cows and the squealing of the young. Elephant babies are big at birth— about 200 pounds—and grow rapidly into playful and some-

times disobedient youngsters. While on the march, a mother tries to bring her offspring into line with a slap, and if that proves ineffective, may uproot a bush and switch the rebel over the back. But she is also extremely gentle and solicitous. With her all-purpose trunk, she bathes the baby, pushes it up steep embankments and even carries it across streams. Seldom does the youngster leave her side until it is about two years old, because of the danger from marauding lions. In her lifetime of 40 to 50 years, a single cow produces a dozen or more young —most of which stay with "the family" until their teens.

4

The Carnivores

THE spectacular diversity of the plains fauna of Africa is not restricted to the herbivores. In all the world no place can match the African savannas as a hunting ground for meat-eating animals.

If you should come upon a scrap of dried rawhide from a young Thomson's gazelle, say, somehow overlooked by scavengers, it might not be an easy job to identify the killer. In fact, in parts of Africa the predator would have to be sought among some two dozen different kinds of carnivorous mammals. Most likely it would have been one of the more inveterate killers of antelopes—lion, leopard, cheetah or the Cape hunting dog. But any one of three kinds of hyenas might have been involved, or a jackal or even a bat-eared fox. Or it could have been one of the smaller cats—the serval, the caracal or the gray cat. The civet, genet and several sorts of mongoose would have to be canvassed, too. Nor could the ratel, the burrowing honey badger and others of the weasel family be wholly ruled out. To make the point even stronger, the slayer of the gazelle might not have been a mammal at all, but any of a long list of raptorial birds able to prey on any very little antelope. Crocodiles feed on gazelles, too, and so do pythons. They could both be eliminated in the present search, because neither leaves any scraps; but throughout the wild country their inroads must be reckoned along with those made by warm-blooded killers.

It is primarily an exchange of energy, through the processes of eating and being eaten, that organizes living things into communities. In any self-supporting community the original capture of energy is made by green plants. This energy is then harvested by plant eaters of various kinds and sizes. On the African plains the chief harvesters are the hoofed mammals. They in turn are killed and eaten by predators. Such links in food-getting activity make up a relationship known as a food chain, although a series of feeding relationships is rarely as direct as the food-chain metaphor suggests. Hardly ever can a single kind of herbivore be found eating only one kind of plant and being preyed upon by only one kind of predator. In some environments feeding relations stay simple; in most, however, they become very complicated. The plants are grazed, browsed or uprooted by herbivores of many sizes, working in many different ways and at different times of day and season. There are, thus, alternate channels by which the energy can flow through the ecosystem. And up at the predator level, there may be side paths in the feeding too: the carnivores may eat each other, or part of the energy may dribble out into fleas, ticks or other parasites that infest the killers.

If its complexity has been arrived at naturally—by a slow process of natural adjustment, and not by abrupt invasions—an environment will be a self-sustaining entity in spite of, actually partly *because* of, the violence that goes on in it. The ruthless attacks upon the vegetation and upon the eaters of vegetation are not ruthless and disruptive at all. They are part of a many-sided, delicately adjusted cooperative harvesting process, slowly worked out as the forces of natural selection mold each individual species in it. In fact, the shaping of the community and its workings comes about through the shaping of the component species, and not by any other way.

IN the evolution of communities of organisms, as in the evolution of organisms themselves, there is a universal tendency toward increasing complexity. There are two ways in which a biological landscape can become diverse. One is to be heavily stratified, as ecologists say, composed of tiers, or layers, one upon another. This of course requires development in the third dimension, depth. In such deep environments—a pond, for instance, or a forest, or a coral reef—there is added chance for light to be caught and utilized at various levels on its way down before it is finally soaked up by the ground. Another way in which diversity comes is in the fine subdivision of a single layer of the environment into a number of highly specialized niches. This kind of partitioning sets up new paths for energy exchange and makes for a heavier energy flow through the community as a whole. The African savannas teem with an almost unaccountable diversity of animals, and this helps explain their high productivity in animal protein. Other factors are the large size of the animals involved, their life spans and the efficiency with which they use food, all of which come into the picture in complicated ways.

One of the most varied assortments of grazing and browsing ungulates living together in one place anywhere can be seen in the Nairobi National Park, a 44-square-mile tract lying practically at the outskirts of the city of Nairobi. There is also—as might be expected—a great array of different kinds of good-sized predaceous mammals. With such a gang of makers of mayhem in the community, one wonders how they keep out of one another's way. So many kinds of killers converging upon the little Thomson's gazelle suggests scenes of unbridled strife and competition. Actually, however, friction is very rare. Although the lives of coexisting carnivores do touch now and then—as when they indulge their common predilection for gazelle meat—these second-level consumers live for the most part without any bloodletting among themselves. For every case in which they do clash, there are thousands in which they go peacefully along their separate ways, even when grouped in a relatively small area. Otherwise they would not be there at all, and there would be no savanna community like that in the Nairobi National Park.

How such heavily armed, bloodthirsty animals avoid competition among themselves and overexploitation of plant eaters that furnish their food is a complicated question. Three generalizations have at least a little bearing upon it: (1) The killing is a life function, not a pastime; when hunger is satisfied it stops. (2) Despite some overlap in feeding preference, there is no complete, or even very extensive, duplication of roles between any two predators naturally occupying a given region at any given time. In some places hyenas may possibly kill more antelopes than any other predator, but their inroads are made almost wholly upon the helpless, newly born young. These are too small to be important in the diet of lions and leopards. (3) There are built-in controls which relax the pressure on overkilled prey by starving the young of the killer or by inducing him to migrate when scarcity occurs.

Much remains to be learned about the roles of African carnivores before the applicability of these three principles can be shown in any detail. In fact, ecologists even disagree over how important predation is as a factor in controlling sizes of herbivore populations. But the disagreement concerns only the degree, and not the reality, of a working agreement that evolution has built up between the carnivores and the croppers of the plants.

The big four among predators of adult animals are the lion, the leopard, the cheetah and the Cape hunting dog. Although the relative abundance of each of these may vary from place to place and from season to season, they all often may be found hunting in the same places over much of the savannalands of Africa. Even in regions that have been strongly modified by man, the lion remains the dominant predator. Lions kill the biggest prey, and they harvest the most meat. Although figures are lacking, in most game landscapes lions no doubt make up a greater total weight than any other carnivore. Besides being big, fast and powerful, lions gain added efficiency in their hunting by working in loosely organized groups. Consequently, although their usual prey consists of medium-sized animals like zebras, wildebeests or the young of larger kinds, they sometimes bring down mature buffaloes and giraffes. There are even records of lions killing fully grown elephants, hippopotamuses and rhinoceroses. Such escapades should be thought of as aberrant lion behavior, however.

The social group of the lion is known as a pride. A pride can be one family or it can be several—a mixture of adults, cubs and adolescent animals. In Kruger National Park litters of lions were found to vary in number from one or two to four or five. The smallest litters occurred during a time of heavy lion population and corresponding short food supply. The bigger litters were born later when the lion population had been reduced by control measures.

In an absorbing article in *The Journal of Wildlife Management*, Bruce S. Wright has included data on the make-up, history and habits of a pride of lions in Nairobi National Park, consisting of two lionesses and their litters, each of

THE DWARF MONGOOSE

Shaped like an ordinary mongoose but considerably smaller, this active little African species has no burrow of its own but hunts in daylight, traveling in gypsy groups of up to a dozen individuals. It lives on insects, spiders, snails and lizards, many of which it finds in abandoned termite mounds. When frightened, it may use the mound itself as a hiding place, its slender body allowing it to squeeze into remarkably narrow cracks.

four cubs. Wright kept a record of the daily movements of this pride during a period of nearly two years. From the time the cubs were only two months old, the group had a surprisingly wide hunting range. From the beginning, a night's hunting took the two families distances of one to three miles. When the youngest cubs were 20 months old, the pride was moving an average of nearly two miles a night, with a maximum distance of about six miles. The significant aspect of these observations was the mobility of the pride even when it included very young cubs. When the youngest of them were six months old, the pride was found to be hunting on seven out of each 10 nights. Fourteen months later, there were about nine hunting nights in each 10. During a year's hunting activity, the territory covered by this pride was an oblong tract roughly 3.8 by 8.7 miles, with an area of some 33 square miles.

Lions usually hunt cooperatively. One technique is for the female to hide in the grass, downwind from a band of antelopes, while the male circles around to the upwind side. Then, with his scent streaming down toward the prey, he lets out a roar, the antelopes bolt, and the female springs out on one of them, digging her claws into its head, often breaking its neck in the impact of the fall.

Wright thus described a typical lion hunt that he saw in Ngorongoro Crater:

"The lionesses came out of the reeds where the pride was lying up in the middle of the afternoon and spread out in the grass and lay down. The combined stalk started when the prey animals grazed within striking distance of where the predators were lying. They seemed to spend as much time waiting for the prey to feed up to them as they did in trying to stalk it. When they moved in the 2-foot-high grass, they walked with heads low in a sway-backed slouching gait which showed nothing above the grass. Each lioness in the hunting team raised her head individually to look at the game; rarely were two heads up together. They moved ahead 20 yards at a time and lay down, moving one at a time.

"When six lionesses were in the hunting team they were in crescent formation 50 yards across, about 375 yards from a mixed herd of Thomson's gazelles and a few zebras. The crescent gradually moved toward the feeding herd, and in one hour it moved forward only about 100 yards. By 5:15 p.m. the light was beginning to fail and the hunting team was still 250 yards from the herd. Meanwhile two adult males and a large number of cubs of various sizes had come out of the cover and were lying in the dying sun watching the lionesses. A total of 30 lions was in sight. The cubs began to follow the lionesses, and several about one-third grown joined the hunting crescent. When darkness closed the observation there were nine lionesses and cubs in a crescent 175 yards across moving up on the herd. Next morning a Thomson's gazelle kill, with a lion-killed hyaena beside it, was found about 300 yards from where the lions were last seen the evening before."

N EXT in size to the lion, and individually even more agile and athletic as a killer, is the leopard. In its various geographic races, the leopard has a tremendous range through the Old World. It is found from the borders of the Black Sea in Europe through Arabia, India and Ceylon, into Burma, the Malay Peninsula and up into Siberia, and over most of Africa. Throughout much of this territory, the leopard lives, or once lived, in places inhabited also by either lions or tigers. Lions and tigers, on the contrary, are almost nowhere found together, which suggests that they have similar ecologic roles, while the role of the leopard is unlike that of either of the bigger cats.

The leopard is not a social hunter. It usually hunts alone, and although this limits the size of the prey that can be taken, it does not limit it very narrowly. The strength, agility and hunting acumen of leopards are, on a per-pound basis, probably greater than those of the lion. In any case, they are sufficient to allow a leopard to hunt and kill an antelope heavier than itself and then to climb a tree with it, or to jump through the window of a house, snatch up a dog —to which leopards seem strangely partial—lying by its master, and then be back out of the window and away before the householder can find and unlimber a gun, or even throw a shoe.

Leopards hunt mostly at night, by either ambuscade or stalking. The best leopard habitat is gallery forest along watercourses, or dense brush around water holes in tree savanna. Although the leopard is also an able tracker, its usual hunting technique is to lie in wait beside a water hole or by a well-used trail, often on an overhanging limb. The charge of a leopard at the end of a stalk is probably as fast as that made by any cat except the cheetah.

Out of 420 prey animals killed by leopards in Kruger National Park in 1958 and 1959, 342, or 80 per cent, were impalas. The rest were a miscellaneous lot including young waterbucks, zebras, wildebeests, elands, duikers, cane rats and such birds as guinea fowl.

In places where warthogs are numerous, leopards, and lions, too, show a marked predilection for them as prey. Throughout the dry, rocky parts of Africa, baboons also seem to be a staple. Although leopards are usually too wise to risk an attack on a baboon colony, they evidently take strays quite frequently, and in places where leopards have been killed out, baboons have increased to levels disastrous to local agriculture.

THIRD in size among African cats is the cheetah, or hunting leopard, generally regarded as the swiftest of the cats and perhaps of all running animals. Although cheetahs are colored somewhat like leopards and reach comparable weights, they are very different in build. Their necks and legs are curiously long and doglike, and their heads seem undersized. Their claws are not fully retractile, and cheetahs are not skilled climbers, although they often run up leaning trunks or jump into the low branches of trees.

The top speed of a charging cheetah seems somewhat in doubt. Perhaps it is as much as 70 or 75 miles an hour. In any case, it is sufficient to let a cheetah run down nearly any of the antelopes, provided the distance of the chase is not over four or five hundred yards. Like other cats, cheetahs tire and slow down quickly after the first explosive sprint of their charge.

The cheetah is a grassland animal. It avoids forest and dense brush, and hunts mostly by daylight, often in pairs or small family groups. Although the prey of cheetahs is essentially the same as that of leopards, the hunting technique is very different. Instead of lying in ambush as the leopard usually does, the cheetah approaches a potential victim as closely as possible by flattening itself against the ground. After a prolonged stalk, it suddenly charges and bears down on the prey at a burning speed, jumping onto its back or seizing it by the throat from the side.

The predominant food of cheetahs is the smaller antelopes. In the Kruger National Park, 47 out of 65 kills attributed to cheetahs were impalas. In a study made in Kenya and Tanganyika, 7 out of 12 identified victims of cheetahs were Thomson's gazelles. The total diet is of course highly miscellaneous and includes most of the small mammals of the locality, as well as guinea hens, francolins and other birds.

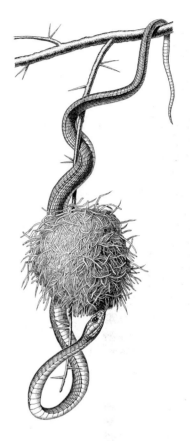

THE SUPPLE BOOMSLANG

Among the smaller African predators are many venomous tree snakes, of which the boomslang is one of the most lethal. Ordinarily it lies hidden in the foliage, waiting for a quick strike at any small lizard or bird that comes within range. It also raids the nests of weaverbirds, as shown here. These nests are often built on the ends of long twigs and have their entrances at the bottom as a protection against marauders. But the boomslang —slender, supple and up to six feet long —slips silently down the branch, inserts its head and seizes the occupant inside.

Although the cheetah is the quintessence of dynamic ferocity in attacking its prey, it is by far the most easily tamed of the big cats and makes the most satisfactory pet. The fully grown male seldom develops the tendency to the sudden fits of annoyance that make leopards so disappointing to people who rear them from their cuddly cubhood, and then suddenly find themselves partly eviscerated for their pains.

The most highly organized hunting team among African predators is that of the Cape hunting dog. This animal is built like a small, stout wolf, four feet long from its nose to the end of its bushy tail. In color it is a mottled yellow, black and white, or sometimes almost completely yellow or black. It has a big head and a swollen facial region. This wide face under a pair of big, rounded ears makes the hunting dog look quite a lot like a hyena, although the two are actually unrelated.

Hunting dogs travel in packs ranging in size from small families to groups of 60 or more. Although they themselves are said to be terrified by the presence of lions, in the eyes of the plains game, hunting dogs seem to be a more frightening menace than even the lion is. Herds of antelope often graze unconcernedly close to a pride of lions—but when hunting dogs come into the territory, they may show great alarm and run away for miles, even when not chased by the dogs. Sometimes they even move away when they hear the distant calling of the hunting dogs, long before the pack has come into view.

Although the main prey of the hunting dog is the smaller kinds of antelopes, the packs sometimes kill big animals—sable antelopes and wildebeests for example. Of 10 recorded wild-dog kills, seven were Thomson's gazelles, one was a wildebeest, one an impala, and one a reedbuck. Thomson's gazelles were the staple diet of the pack Wright studied—a family of two adults and four pups. He described what he called a typical hunt by this group as follows:

"The female cantered off across the plain, leaving the male with the four pups walking slowly behind. The game scattered ahead of her and she passed quite close to several groups of Thomson's gazelles without deviating from her course. Two hundred yards ahead and directly in front of her a Thomson's gazelle turned and ran on the same course the dog was following with the curious gait known as 'stotting,' in which all four feet strike the ground together. This was the one gazelle that was panic-stricken at the sight of the approaching dog, which immediately centered her attention on the gazelle. The dog broke into a gallop, passing through a closer group of gazelles, to follow the animal that had started to run before the dog was close.

"The gazelle was between one and two hundred yards ahead. The dog was still at a steady gallop. The gazelle began to circle the plain and the dog narrowed the gap by cutting across the arc, and closed to about one hundred yards. The gazelle still did not appear excessively frightened and was still bounding along well within the limit of its speed. The chase had now continued for about 2 miles in a half-circle. During this period the pups had lain down in the grass and the male had left them and was lost to sight. Suddenly, as upon receiving a signal, the female increased her speed to the utmost, and the now startled gazelle bounded ahead with frequent glances behind. When its attention was concentrated upon the pursuing dog, the male rose from the grass within 10 feet of the gazelle as it passed. He was beside it in one bound and laid open its flank just behind the ribs with one slashing bite. This knocked the gazelle to the ground, and the dog thrust his head into the wound to the ears and jerked backward with all his weight, carrying with him almost the entire contents of the body cavity. The pups then joined their parents at the kill."

Although the lion, leopard, cheetah and wild dog are the big killers of the hoofed animals of Africa, killing is also done by other species of carnivorous mammals too small to live wholly on ungulates, or which make the main part of their living as scavengers. Some of the smaller mammals are redoubtable hunters, limited in their killing exploits only by their own size. The strongest of these is the caracal, a tawny cat with tufted black ears, which may weigh up to 40 pounds. The caracal has the uncatlike look and almost unbelievable speed of the cheetah, but is much smaller. Caracals are so fast in their movements that when let loose in a flock of pigeons on the ground they have been known to kill half a dozen or more before the birds get into the air, and then to spring two yards up to snatch another of them down. The caracal is found in most of the warm, dry regions from Arabia to northern India, and in Africa all the way from the Mediterranean to the Cape of Good Hope.

Other savannaland predators are the serval and the fierce little gray cat, which live mainly on ground birds, hares and rodents, but sometimes are able to overpower little hoofed animals. The bat-eared fox is a diminutive killer sometimes able to bring down the young of the smaller ungulates.

An occasional predator that may be of more importance as a factor in the lives of some species of antelope than is generally known is the baboon. There appears to be little information on its role as a killer of antelopes, but it is widely accused by Africans and hunters.

Other sometime killers of little or newly born antelopes are scavengers, such as jackals, hyenas and the carrion-eating vultures. There is rarely any carrion left lying about an African plain. No dead body lasts long on the veld. If the killer does not eat it all, it may go to feed a dozen kinds of hangers-on and cleaners-up. Lions at a kill sometimes spend more time trying to keep vultures, jackals and hyenas away than they do in eating. All the scavengers—bird and mammal alike—occasionally do their own killing, especially when any small reverse at birth keeps a baby antelope from getting at once to its feet and joining the herd. Even the pious-looking secretary bird manages to take a small toll in the same way.

T HE many unknown aspects of predation as an ecologic factor in the plains community will have to be understood before any intelligent management of the national parks, reserves and game areas can be carried out. These are only beginning to be studied. Theoretically, a useful outcome of predation on the game herds is the weeding out of weaker individuals. That such an effect does indeed operate in some cases seems clear. However, the weeding out of the weak is mostly not done by the big confirmed killers, but instead by the more casual predators such as hyenas, jackals and birds. Some surprising statistics suggest that the large predators kill mostly mature, healthy prey. Data on 211 kills in Kenya and Tanganyika showed that animals at or just after the prime of life, and not the young, sick or newly born, made up 65 per cent of the kills. By far the greater part of the animals killed had been in good health and feeding condition. These observations raise the question of how important predators really are in controlling the populations of herbivores, particularly when the depredations of lions, say, must be weighed against the epidemics or famines that seem to come with any overabundance of a species.

The French mammalogist François Bourlière, after looking over the scattered

THREATS AS A DEFENSE

Although baboons catch occasional small animals, they are mostly vegetarian and are themselves hunted by large predators. However, they are also good at defending themselves and have a vivid way of reminding a potential attacker that they are dangerous. This is by adopting the so-called threat position shown here. In it, a baboon will stand lightly on all fours, with teeth bared. Its hair is raised and its head thrust forward, making the animal look a good deal larger than it is. It will roll its eyes and stamp the ground with a forepaw, its whole attitude one of aggressive assurance. Few predators are rash enough to tangle with a group of mature threatening baboons.

information available from African national parks, made some interesting generalizations on predation in the African savanna country. He showed, for instance, that killers favor some species over others among the mixed antelope herds. Their choice is not influenced by abundance, even in cases in which the antelopes in question are of comparable size. In several East African parks, almost half of the identified kills were wildebeests, and only 15 per cent were zebras, although at the time of the survey wildebeests outnumbered zebras by only about one third. In the same park, although hartebeests were almost half as numerous as wildebeests, hartebeests figured in only 2 per cent of the kills. In Kruger National Park, wildebeests seem even more avidly sought after. Although less abundant than zebras there, and 20 times less numerous than impalas, they made up 25 per cent of identified kills, while impalas were killed in 23 per cent of the cases and zebras in only 13 per cent.

One implication of these figures is that some kinds of herbivores bear the main burden of feeding some kinds of predators. Another is that the preferences the carnivores show help keep them from stepping on one another's toes.

Although the predators of a given region usually avoid conflict among themselves, cases of violent encounter do sometimes occur. There are widespread tales, some apocryphal no doubt, but some surely true, of titanic battles between lions and leopards, between lions and crocodiles, between pythons and crocodiles, and so on—through any combination one may think of. In *African Wildlife*, Ranger Pieter Lorentz of the Kruger National Park tells of an incident that illustrates the kind of ill feeling that sometimes occurs among the eaters of meat:

"At the Rabelais Dam at about 5 p.m. I saw two lions that had pulled down a blue wildebeest. After about an hour four jackal and eight hyena had arrived on the scene, apparently wanting their share of the carcass, but keeping some distance away. A leopard also crept slowly nearer to see whether perhaps he too might get something. The keen eyes of the jackals soon spotted the leopard and they began to shriek. The leopard then went for a drink of water and the jackals followed him. Each time he stopped the jackals did likewise. When he began to drink they gave vent to a full-blooded scream. After about five minutes a further four jackals arrived and they also began to howl as loudly as possible. They all ran round the leopard, which was still busy drinking. The howling certainly proved too much for the leopard, for he beat a hasty retreat.

"The jackals' performance served its purpose, for later on they were able to obtain a trifle to eat."

WRIGHT recorded a few definite cases of such strife in the East African parks. In Nairobi National Park, for instance, a cheetah was caught asleep and killed by lions. A caracal was killed by a python. Wild dogs were occasionally killed and eaten by leopards. A single wild dog bitch was seen to drive away a hyena. The Tanzania Game Department has two records of lions being killed by elephants which they evidently had attacked at a water hole. A black-backed jackal was found killed by a leopard.

But these are only side issues, the occasional alterations of the ecologic machinery. The important thing to remember about lions is not that they sometimes fight among themselves or with other formidable killers, or that they occasionally get killed by elephants. It is that, although superbly rigged out for violence, they mainly kill only in ways and degrees that keep the kind of community they live in working on smoothly through the ages.

A FULL-FED CHEETAH SAUNTERS BY A GROUP OF UNALARMED GAZELLES. IF IT WERE HUNGRY, ITS STEALTHY BEHAVIOR WOULD WARN THEM

Hunters and Spongers

In the course of their existence, the animals of the great African savanna have become closely dependent upon each other. The predators kill only what they need, and when they finish eating, a host of scavengers picks every scrap of meat from the carcass. Even the hunted benefit from the system, for without predators they would multiply until the food was exhausted, and all would starve.

95

A LEOPARD LURKS in the tall grass of Serengeti National Park. The most maligned of the great cats, it has a reputation for being a wanton killer. But the facts do not support the charge. Although a hungry leopard will sometimes kill more game than it can eat at one time, it usually returns to the car-cass many times before it goes after fresh quarry; even the most putrefied meat will not repel a leopard. A more efficient hunter than the cheetah or lion, it dispatches its prey quickly, severing the jugular vein or neck vertebrae with one clean bite. It then drags the carcass into the underbrush, skillfully disem-

bowels it and buries the entrails. After savoring the delicacies —heart, liver, lungs, nose, tongue and even the ears, the leopard begins to eat in earnest, bolting great chunks of skin and flesh until it is satiated. Frequently it will carry the remains of a kill high into a tree to foil jackals and hyenas. A veteran hunter once saw a giraffe calf weighing at least 200 pounds lying across a branch a dozen feet above the ground. For some unknown reason, vultures will not touch a leopard's tree larder. Leopards are characteristically wary, but when wounded they fight ferociously and are actually more dangerous than lions.

DRAPED IN THE BRANCHES OF A TREE, EIGHT LIONS TRY TO ESCAPE BITING FLIES AND THE OPPRESSIVE HEAT. FEMALES AND YOUNG MALES ARE

The Lethargic King of Beasts

When they are not hunting or patrolling their territory, lions are the laziest of the big cats. On any hot day, and particularly after a satisfying meal, they lounge about in a state of virtual immobility. Except during mating season, they are gregarious creatures, living together in prides that sometimes number more than a dozen individuals. Lions are also noisy in the extreme, emitting sounds that range from almost inaudible moans to the stentorian roars that one naturalist has called "inexpressibly grand . . . the most sublime sound in nature."

A RHINOCEROS WINS a brief territorial squabble with a pair of lions resting in Ngorongoro Crater in Tanganyika. These animals generally ignore each other, although lions are some-

LIGHT AND AGILE ENOUGH TO CLIMB UP INTO LOW BRANCHES, BUT THE HEAVIER MALES ARE USUALLY LEFT PANTING DROWSILY ON THE GROUND

times known to eat young rhinos, and on rare occasions a hungry pride will kill a full-grown adult. Lions are unwilling to exert themselves except when absolutely necessary. This is quite evident here, for they do not budge until the rhino is only a few feet away. Then, after a few angry growls, the lion trots off with its mate, leaving the field to the larger beast.

GUARDING HIS MEAL from intruders, a lion stands over a dead zebra. Lions can and do eat practically everything, including rats, pythons, ostriches and baboons. But their favorite diet consists of zebra and wildebeest, which are plentiful and relatively easy to kill. When they are particularly ambitious, lions add buffaloes, giraffes and even young elephants to their menu.

Etiquette in the Pride

After the pride makes a kill, a priority system goes into effect that differs drastically from the procedure in most other animal societies. The adult males eat first, gorging themselves with no thought for the females and cubs. Ironically, females bring in most of the food, except when the males help to kill a giraffe or a buffalo. If the kill happens to be large enough (it usually is), there will be enough for the entire pride, perhaps for several days. But the females and young must wait patiently for the males to finish, and cubs occasionally die of starvation. Fortunately, the newly born cubs are raised separately by their mothers, who usually see to it that the youngsters eat first. But when they are between one and two years old, the cubs must learn to accept their status at the foot of the table.

TAKING THEIR TURN at the carcass, lionesses begin their meal. While the male was eating, one of them snuggled up to him. When he stopped growling, she knew it was safe to move in.

101

A YEAR-OLD CUB IS FIRST IN LINE FOR A DINNER OF REEDBUCK. IN A FEW MONTHS HE MAY BE LAST

Garbagemen of the Savannas

Such is the economy of nature that no food is wasted on the plains. When there is a kill, an army of scavengers surrounds the carcass, milling about until the predator is satiated or can no longer endure their heckling. The first to eat are the ill-tempered hyenas and the quick little jackals, who dart in and out trying to avoid the hyenas' crushing jaws. Then the vultures move in, plunging their heads deep into the carcass and ripping out the putrefied entrails with their beaks. As disgusting as their habits may seem, scavengers perform the indispensable service of keeping the plains free of carrion.

SCAVENGERS WAIT FOR A LION TO FINISH WITH A GIRAFFE CARCASS. THE

UNABLE TO CONTROL THEIR HUNGER ANY LONGER, A PACK OF HYENAS RUSHES THE CARCASS. IF A SINGLE HYENA SHOULD BE BRASH ENOUGH TO TRY

YENAS STARTED ARRIVING, ALONG WITH THE JACKAL, WHEN THEY SAW THE VULTURES BEGIN THEIR LONG, SWEEPING DESCENT TO THE GROUND

HIS, HE WOULD SURELY BE KILLED, BUT A PACK CAN DRIVE A LION INTO A FRENZY OF FRUSTRATION AND EVEN MAKE IT LEAVE THE KILL ENTIRELY

Realm of the Lesser Hunters

The glamor of "bring 'em back alive" and the big game safari has overshadowed the smaller carnivores of the African savanna, even though the latter are more numerous. They account for a great number of kills and can be as savage as the largest predators. So fearsome are the Cape hunting dogs that leopards scramble into trees to avoid them. In fact, no predatory animal in Africa is responsible for more disturbance. Hunting in packs, they lope after their prey and tear out flesh until the prey drops. Within moments, they devour the carcass and set out in search of another victim.

The long-legged caracals are not as relentless as the indefatigable wild dogs, but they can easily out-

THE CARACAL, whose name means black-eared in Turkish, was prized for its beautiful fur and was in danger of extinction until it was protected by game laws.

THE CAPE HUNTING DOG, unlike true dogs, has only four toes on each of its forefeet; it also has a decidedly unpleasant body odor. It kills fresh food for every meal.

run small antelopes. They also eat birds, including the predators. Caracals are known to attack and kill martial eagles, among the most powerful of all birds of prey. The less aggressive serval can kill young reedbucks and impalas, but normally hunts small rodents and birds. The aardwolf preys almost exclusively on termites, which it laps up with its long sticky tongue. During lean seasons it steals eggs, eats a few locusts and beetles and an occasional bit of abandoned carrion. When it is frightened, its long, dark mane stands erect, making it look quite ominous. Altogether there are about a dozen other species of African carnivores, each in its own way of vital importance to the ecological community.

THE SERVAL, like most small mammals on the plains, prefers to rear its litters underground. This handsome serval kitten was probably born in an aardvark's burrow.

THE AARDWOLF is related to the hyenas but feeds mostly on termites. It was named by the Dutch, who called it "earth wolf" because it lived in underground burrows.

A DUNG BEETLE scurries along with a large manure ball it has scooped and patted into shape with its spiked front legs. It uses the manure for food or as a place in which to lay an egg.

A TREASURE TROVE of dung balls is uncovered by a ranger in Rhodesia's Wankie National Park. Beetles hollowed out a chamber about a foot beneath the ground to store the balls in.

Dung Eaters and Blood Drinkers

Carnivores are not the only creatures that depend upon herbivores for food. The savanna seethes with a variety of insects that feed on them both directly and indirectly. Many of these, like the dung beetle, pose no threat to animals or humans. But the tsetse fly is such a menace that entire populations have fled before it. Domestic animals succumb so readily to a parasite it carries that there are great stretches in Central Africa where they simply cannot exist. Thousands of humans have died of the same disease, prompting an all-out war on tsetse flies that has sometimes ended in foolish and tragic consequences. In Uganda, for instance, large game was blamed as being the primary source of the disease, and more than 60,000 wild animals were slaughtered. But the fly remained, as deadly as ever. Insecticides are being used with considerable success, and hitherto perilous areas are becoming fit for human habitation —an ominous development for the savanna wildlife.

A TSETSE FLY settles on the arm of a naturalist. Its danger is that it may suck in microscopic parasites— called trypanosomes—along with the blood of the host animal. These mature in a few weeks inside the fly and may be transmitted to the next animal that the fly bites. If it is a human being, sleeping sickness may result.

A THREE-INCH BALL has a crusted outer covering that prevents the inside from drying out, leaving a moist, nutritious food supply that the larva inside will feed on for a few weeks.

THE SAME BALL OPENED reveals a live larva eating the walls of its nest. A few weeks after the egg hatches, the larva becomes a chrysalis; in another month an adult beetle emerges.

LONG, STRONG TALONS enable an African hawk eagle to get a secure grasp on the large game birds it feeds upon. The fleshy pads under its toes give it a good grip on slippery feathers.

ARMORED LEGS and a thick pad of feathers on its chest give the brown harrier eagle a decided advantage over snakes. This one is swallowing a viper it has killed with its talons.

THE LARGE, HOOKED BEAK of the martial eagle can tear a carcass in half if it is too heavy to be carried to the nest. Its owner is the most powerful predatory bird on the open savanna.

Hunters on the Wing

Nowhere in the world is there such a large congregation of birds of prey as on the African savanna. They range in size from the huge vultures that feed on dead elephants and rhinoceroses down through the powerful eagles that are capable of killing small antelopes to the two-ounce pygmy falcons with their diet of insects.

Ordinarily each species goes its separate way, avoiding serious competition with other predators by having well-defined hunting habits of its own. A single hilltop in East Africa was recently found to have no fewer than nine species of raptorial birds living on it, none of them interfering with any of the others. Long-crested eagles preyed on rats and snakes that they found above 4,500 feet, whereas Wahlberg's eagles preferred to hunt for the same creatures below 4,000 feet. A soaring species, Verreaux's eagle, caught hyraxes living on rocky hillsides but it ignored ones in thicker cover; these were hunted by still another eagle, the crowned, which swooped down on them from perches in trees.

SCAVENGERS TURNED HUNTERS, marabou storks stand at the edge of a grass fire to snap up fleeing mice and lizards. The smoke also attracts eagles, kites, vultures and secretary birds.

5

The Tropical Rain Forest

As a place in which to see hosts of big animals of many kinds standing about a sweeping landscape, the *Acacia* savannas of Africa have no equal in the world. But for sheer biological complexity, it is the tropical rain forest that cannot be matched. It is the most advanced and intricate natural organization on earth. Its inner workings have nowhere been adequately studied; but enough is known to be sure that in most of the warm lowlands of the tropical world, if some seven feet of rain falls each year and no month has less than two inches, the community that develops there will represent organized life at its peak.

Of the three great rain-forest areas of the world—African, Asian and American—that of Africa is the smallest. It occupies two main areas, both lying between the Sudan on the north and the Angola plateau to the south. The smaller of these tracts, known as the Upper Guinea forest, occupies the lowlands from Liberia to eastern Ghana, where it is interrupted by the savanna country of Dahomey. The Lower Guinea block is also called simply the Congo forest. It begins as a narrow strip along the coast of eastern Nigeria, fans out in the Cameroons and Gabon, then flows across the floor of the great Congo basin, extending eastward to the Mountains of the Moon and the slopes of the East Africa plateau.

Only a few thousand years ago, the rain forest in Africa was a great deal bigger than it is today. At other times it has been smaller, or at least differently distributed in the lowlands. This is suggested by the present ranges of rain-forest animals, which fall into patterns that can only be explained by supposing that repeated interruptions of the rain forest occurred during the Pleistocene. The territory occupied by a species or a group of species often begins or ends without apparent reason—in what seems to be a perfectly homogeneous habitat, with no barriers of any kind in sight. These curious patterns of distribution are among the most interesting puzzles of African zoogeography.

Looking at the two separate tracts of rain forest on the map, one might expect them to have different bird faunas, for example, simply because they are separated from each other by grasslands inhospitable to forest birds. And to an extent this is true—a number of the Upper Guinea birds are different from those of the Congo forest. However, many of the differences do not show up where they logically should—at the natural barriers that separate the forest tracts. Unaccountably, the ranges of most of the forest species end within the spread of the evergreen forest itself. According to the British ornithologist R. E. Moreau, of all the differences between the bird faunas of the Upper Guinea and Congo forests, only about a quarter appear where one would expect them.

A similar puzzle is revealed by the distribution of rain-forest mammals. The chimpanzees and tree hyraxes of the western Congo forest are closer kin to those living hundreds of miles away in the Upper Guinea forest than they are to the chimpanzees and tree hyraxes that live just across the Niger River from them in their own Congo forest block. The only sensible explanation for perplexing bits of evidence like this seems to be that the rain forest itself has changed its shape and size in the fairly recent past. The English biologist A. H. Booth believed this to be the case. He made an exhaustive study of all the rain-forest monkeys and lemurs, and suggested that they represent "fossil" distribution—in other words a distribution that once made sense even if it does not now: a holdover from the past when the boundaries of the rain forest and the interruptions between them were not the same as they are today. Speculating about the breaks or interruptions that may have separated sections of earlier forest, Booth decided that they had left more or less intact three areas of rain forest that he referred to as "refuges," tracts of unchanging habitat in which the fauna could hold on during periods when the rest of the country dried out.

It would apparently not take much of a change in climate to reshape the rain-forest blocks. In fact, the plant ecologist Van Zinderen Bakker thinks that a drop of no more than three or four degrees in temperature would lower evaporation rates and raise soil moisture enough to produce a great expansion of the evergreen forest of the continent, both in the mountains and in the lowlands.

The species that live in the rain forest, and the relationships among them, are not only more varied but more specialized than in any other environment. The rain forest did not just happen, any more than an elephant happened. It is a product of natural selection, of slow evolution, in which an increasing number of living things have grown increasingly adept at surviving and reproducing their kind by increasingly refined adjustments to one another. It may be recalled that in Chapter 3 I said much the same thing about the savanna community. The difference is that the organization of the savannas is mostly in two dimensions, whereas the rain forest has depth as well. Its structure runs for 200 feet or more vertically, from the habitat of organisms that live beneath the surface of the ground to the crowns of the tallest trees. If you think of the rain forest not as a mere conglomeration of species but as an organization built and functioning along predictable lines, this question is bound to come to mind: Why did natural selection work upon the rain-forest biota in such a way as to build it into so complicated an edifice?

The question is fair, but the answer is not easy. One might say simply that all organic evolution tends to make more complicated things out of simple ones, and that this trend applies to *organizations* of organisms as well as to the species themselves. This does not really account for the natural selection of rain forests, though, but only recognizes a tendency in evolution. Another thing that could be said is that wherever on earth there are rain forests the climate is very stable. Both temperature and rainfall stay reliably within comfortable limits and thus allow very refined, long-term adjustments to evolve, without setbacks from drought or cold. That, too, is true. But again, it only describes a tendency. It does not identify the selective advantage that caused the biota to be molded into a rain forest.

The more fundamental answer will almost certainly involve energy relations. Besides becoming more diverse as it gets more mature, a forest makes another gain which is probably the really basic one from an evolutionary standpoint. It gains efficiency in its use of energy. The rain forest requires less energy, per pound of live stuff, to support its organization than any other kind of terrestrial environment, although it looks prodigally overstocked and wasteful. But really it is operating with more efficiency—i.e., is more productive—than the plains of Serengeti or a field of Iowa corn. One reason for this is that in the complicated structure of the forest, there are innumerable pathways, innumerable circuits —to use an electrical analogy—for solar energy to take, and thus more chances for it to be changed to biological energy before it finally reaches the ground. It is probably this increased efficiency in use of energy that increased the success of the rain-forest design, and thus of every living thing that makes it up.

The animals of the rain forest live mainly in the trees or beneath the ground. The forest floor in between is inhabited only sparsely by mammals, snakes, amphibians and insects. There are a few ground-dwelling birds—the francolins and rails, for example—and most of the monkeys and squirrels come down to earth after fallen fruits or nuts, or to forage for grubs in logs or leaf mold. But the floor of the forest is not noteworthy for its fauna.

T HE underground zones are another matter. In the tropical rain forest, the fall of organic material, in the form of dead leaves and twigs and animal detritus of all kinds, is constant and heavy. If there were not an army of efficient small scavengers living in the soil to convert this rain of dead material back into living tissue, the whole community would grind to a halt, because gradually the pile-up would be so great that there would be nothing left for the larger forms —either animals or plants—to exploit. That is why the host of insects, tiny arthropods and even tinier bacteria that live in the soil is so important. They are the "decay" agents, the reprocessors which break down dead organic tissue into its chemical constituents and, in one way or another, turn it back into protoplasm again. Not much is known about the soil ecology of the rain-forest interior, but it is easy to see that it is a region of furious activity and great opportunity, as is the region of the high trees above it, where sunlight can come

WALLED IN
FOR THE DURATION

For protection against predators, the silvery-cheeked hornbill chooses a hollow tree for a nest and then seals herself in until her chicks are grown. This drawing shows a cutaway of a nest with the female receiving a berry from her spouse through the entrance hole, which has been closed to a narrow opening by a mixture of mud, bark and material regurgitated by the male. The female does the plastering job herself, working first from the outside, then squeezing through the narrowing slit to complete it from within. She and her chicks are fed 10 to 20 times a day over a three-month period, and one male was estimated to have delivered 24,000 fruits to his family during confinement. The female keeps the nest clean, throwing out dirt and old feathers, and defecating neatly through the opening. When the young are grown, she hammers down the wall with her bill and emerges, so fat and flabby that for a few days she can scarcely fly.

streaming in and where energy exchange can also take place on a large scale. An acre of rain forest, African or any other, is one of the most dynamic acres in the world, but you would never know this just walking through the place.

The roles of the multitudes of animals of the rain-forest community are mostly unknown. It is clear enough that there is a highly organized and complex interplay of forces; it is equally clear that the forest is a product of natural selection and that it exists only because each part of it raises the life expectancy of every other part. But proving this is another matter, since most of it still rests on circumstantial evidence. This gives ecology a bad name among the kinds of biologists who are able to make nice, precise analyses and predictions of the events they study. Any ecologist knows perfectly well that each animal has a niche in the organization of the tropical evergreen forest. The whole concept of the ecosystem, the most important integrating idea in the field of ecology, depends upon this being so. And yet, far from knowing all the ways in which each rain-forest animal affects and is affected by the environment, we do not in many cases even have adequate lists showing what animals are there. How could we make such lists, when some of the animals have not yet been discovered, let alone given names by taxonomists?

One thing ecologists want to know about a biological community is the biomass of its component animals—the total weight of monkey meat per acre, for instance, or of toad protoplasm per hectare. The dearth of such information for the rain forest is astonishing. François Bourlière recently gathered up all the data he could find on population densities and biomass in the different types of African communities. For the evergreen forest, he found almost nothing. The only quantitative data that could be located were in a table published by W. B. Collins in his book *The Perpetual Forest*. The table was based on counts made by a timber-cruising party that marked every tree in an area of 100 square miles in the Tano Nimri Forest Reserve in Ghana and counted every mammal seen or killed during a four-month stay in the forest. The tally unfortunately did not include the squirrels, which surely made up a major element in the biomass of the tract, as they do in all lowland African rain forest.

The estimates of the numbers of different species in Collins' chart were: 140 diana monkeys; 126 mona monkeys; 818 black, 613 red and 5 olive colobus monkeys; 83 crowned mangabeys; 20 chimpanzees; 61 Maxwell's duikers; 29 bay duikers; 5 royal antelopes; 31 pangolins; 29 porcupines; 2 civets; 9 snakes (species not given); and "numerous" squirrels and other rodents.

As incomplete as this lone quantitative sample is, it does confirm a few things that we know about rain-forest inhabitants. Hoofed animals are scarce; this, of course, is due to the dearth of green stuff in the lower levels of the woods. To harvest the rain-forest pastures, one must climb. Monkeys and rodents climb, and in dense lowland woods they are the predominating primary consumers.

THE most striking feature of the rain forest as an ecological structure is its vertical stratification. In this respect the forest is like a deep lake. The treetops shut out direct light from the ground and cut down on the wind, and, as in a lake, the deeper one goes the quieter it is and the darker it is. This makes possible the development of a layered structure in the forest, based primarily on the amount of sunlight that filters down from layer to layer. The strata that result are not sharply cut off from one another. On the contrary, they are closely interwoven, not only through the constant movement of animals from one layer to another but also by the passage of water and chemicals up and down in the intricate plumbing systems of the plants, and by the rain of material ceaselessly dropping from the trees to the ground. All layers are interdependent.

The powerhouse of the forest is the green canopy at the top. This is the layer that is exposed to the full sunlight and consequently the one in which nearly all the photosynthesis goes on. The canopy is also responsible for much of the greenhouselike tranquillity of the climate beneath it. The crowns of the trees make a tightly set mosaic. Each tree is shaped to fit whatever space is available after its quiet, biochemical pushing and shoving with neighbors has been impressed upon its systems of growth. Seen from a slow airplane flying over the rain forest, the faceted structure of the roof is both obvious and elegant. It is strong proof of the fine balance between the processes of competition and co-operation in the forest organization, and is as well demonstrated by individual leaves as by entire tree crowns. It is well known that each leaf of a tree competes for a place in the sun; but there is a point at which they desist in their quiet strife, bend about to accept some less advantageous place or just fall off if no compromise is possible. The same competition happens among the separate tree crowns of the forest canopy.

THE unbroken continuity of the high green layers of the rain forest is important to the animals of the forest in another way. By moving upward or downward only slightly as it travels, any animal able to grasp twigs can walk across the forest indefinitely and can claim a home range and territory for itself just as a fox or elk does on the ground. Some treetop animals, like monkeys, save time by jumping gaps or by swinging across empty spaces. Others, like the African scaly-tailed flying squirrel, span them with long glides sustained by extended folds of skin between fore and hind limbs. But many of the canopy animals—insects, reptiles and some of the mammals—very deliberately crawl, walk or move hand over hand across the forest, never letting go of one twig until they have grasped another. There are even many kinds of birds that move about this way. While most of the birds of the canopy are able to fly well, many of them spend their days creeping about among the twigs or walking the limbs, as the hornbills, the parrots and the brilliantly colored touracos do. To touracos, there are open paths in the treetops, and they run pell-mell along them from one tree to another when anxious to be quickly elsewhere.

THE MONKEY KILLER

Gliding swiftly among the lofty treetops of the rain-forest canopy, the crowned eagle has earned the nickname "leopard of the air" because of its deadly attacks on monkeys. This bird relies in its hunting on surprise, on noiseless flight and on its maneuverability, made possible by rounded wings and an extremely flexible tail. It usually manages to strike a monkey on a branch before it can get away, and if the prey is not large, it eats it then and there, devouring the heart, spleen and liver first and letting the bones fall one by one to the ground.

115

To all these animals, the continuity of the forest roof is a main factor in their lives, and their being in it draws up the meat eaters after them, or draws them down—the raptorial birds swoop into the canopy after the monkeys or rodents, like ospreys plunging into the waters of a lake. The genet goes up and patrols the highest reaches of the roof, and the civets and golden cats also hunt freely in the trees. The serval and forest leopard are less foot-loose in the higher levels, but they too have to climb to stay decently fed in the rain forest.

Of backboned animals, the main rain-forest groups are arboreal rodents (mostly squirrels) and the primates—the monkeys, apes and lemurs. The most conspicuous of these, both to the ear and the eye, are members of two monkey subfamilies. One of these is the Colobinae, in which there are four lowland-forest species, all mainly leaf eating. The black-and-white colobus monkeys are among the handsomest of African primates, and some of them, especially the black colobus, are among the noisiest. The other group is the big, diverse subfamily Cercopithecinae. It has at least 15 species in the lowland forest, and many more subspecies. The subfamily includes the mona and diana monkeys, the putty-nosed monkeys, the mangabeys, and the drills and the mandrills—two forest kinsmen of the baboon.

The other rain-forest primates are lorisoid lemurs. These include three kinds of galagos, or bush babies, which range widely outside the forest as well as in it, and four species of pottos, which belong to the loris family. Pottos eat fruits and leaves, are insectivorous and nocturnal. They are probably the only mammals of African forests that never willingly descend from the trees. Their only locomotion is over the pathways of the treetops; on the ground, they are almost helpless. Bosman's potto, the best known of the four, is small, furry and about a foot long, with a short, thick tail and big eyes and hands. The oddest feature of its anatomy is a series of bony projections along its back. These are extensions of the neural spines of the vertebrae, and they protrude right through the flesh, evidently serving as a protective device. The angwantibo, commonly called the golden potto, is a rare and somewhat smaller relative of Bosman's potto. It has no tail and lacks the bony spines along the back. It sleeps curled up in a ball, holding on with all four feet if it is out on a branch, only letting go with one hind paw if it can snuggle back against a tree bole.

These lorises of Africa share with the chameleons, their reptilian colleagues of the treetops, an eccentricity that reaches its peak in the sloths of tropical America and in the slow loris of Asia. Each of these animals moves with the most astonishing and unaccountable deliberation, as if each move might be its last. One is tempted to conclude that this is somehow an adaptive trait, in some unknown way helpful to life in trees. As far as I know, however, the adaptive significance of it has not been explained.

THE most awesome forest primate is the gorilla. Because of the recent amazing studies of George Schaller and John Emlen, it is the mountain gorilla of Uganda and the volcanoes of the eastern Congo that is best known. But there is also a West African race, the lowland gorilla, still represented in a few places in Nigeria, Cameroons and parts of the Congo. In his book *On Safari*, Armand Denis told of a trip he made to get young lowland gorillas for a colony he planned to establish in Florida. To his surprise he found the beasts to be fairly numerous some 300 miles north of Brazzaville near a village called Oka, in what is now the Republic of Congo. He not only found the gorillas but he learned that the people of Oka are traditionally dedicated to hunting

SLOW BUT SURE

With extra strong gripping muscles in its forelimbs, the golden potto makes its way slowly and deliberately in lofty rain forest trees, rarely letting go with more than one of its feet at a time. Even in sleep (below) the muscles grip firmly as it sits, head tucked between its forelegs, high among the branches.

them, not casually or occasionally but as their staple source of meat. The hunts they stage are communal undertakings. Scouts locate sleeping families of gorillas, and the hunters go out and encircle them by quietly chopping pathways in the undergrowth. Sections of net are set up end to end in this circular clearing, completely surrounding the gorillas, which are then driven into the netting and killed with makeshift guns and spears.

The lowland gorilla is not exclusively a resident of the forest interior. Its preferred habitat is the forest edge. The chimpanzee, also a forest animal, is even more partial to forest edge than its huge relative. Both, nevertheless, are confirmed and polished arborealists, and both are mainly vegetarian.

THE most diverse, and probably the most important ecologically, of the rainforest animals are insects. Little is known of their roles and relationships, but their variety is vast, and they surely are a predominating influence in maintaining the organization of the forest community. Not that the rain forest seems insect-ridden to a man walking through it. On the contrary, insect pests are likely to be less bad than in far leaner, open country. In the closed-canopy forest, the insects are, like the rest of the fauna there, strangely inconspicuous. But they are there, nevertheless, and at the peak of their diversity for the whole earth. They are down in the soil, in galleries or nests, or foraging through the leaf mold; they are under bark or hidden by obliterative patterns on the trunks of the trees; and above all, they are up in the teeming treetops. Crickets, katydids and fantastic phasmids reap tons of leaves in billions of tiny bites; moths, butterflies, cicadas and bees lap and suck the juices of trees, fruits or flowers; ants abound in the canopy, and termites lodge there too, although most of the vast array of forest termites live in mounds on the ground. All these are stalked by mantids and chameleons or tweaked up by insectivorous birds. Besides the insects that live genuinely arboreal lives, there are other creatures that ought to be down on the ground but, surprisingly, are up in the trees too. These are soil dwellers—earthworms, mites, minute snails—that inhabit the tiny handfuls of soil, compost or leaf mold that are found aloft in the leaves of epiphytic plants.

Because of their habit of carrying leaves and other food materials underground, the ants and the termites accelerate the conversion of materials and loom very large in the dynamics of the forest. Much of what they do is hidden and rhythmical. But there is one event among ants that comes like an explosion. That is the forays of the driver ants, mass marches that are unpredictable and catastrophic. The ants are said to time their marauding on a sort of schedule, geared to the reproductive cycle. The squirming of the developing pupas of a new generation of ants apparently excites their elders to be off to lay in the stores of animal food the augmented colony will require. They then move through the forest in ordered millions. The deep ranks of workers are flanked by masses of huge, big-headed soldiers. All are kept in their formation by the communal odor—a scent cue that each exudes—the impetus of their quest maintained by the stimulating wriggle of the larval young they carry with them.

To anyone who sees it, the marching of the driver ants is an imposing, even terrifying, thing. The hidden small beings of the forest emerge and flee in unsuspected multitudes before the advancing army. Driver ants have even been known to enter human abodes and smother and chop up the occupants. Among the more impressionable commentators on tropical life and travel, they have been a perennial theme for fervid prose.

FAST AND FAR

Unlike the potto, the scaly-tailed squirrel is extremely mobile, scampering about in trees and launching itself on 150-foot glides from trunk to trunk on its large skin flaps. The scales under its tail have sharp edges, and when the animal is clinging to a tree in a vertical position, they dig into the bark and help support it.

Despite the shivers that these remorseless little creatures give to the average person, they are completely engrossing to the serious zoologist. The many kinds of army and driver ants all belong to a single subfamily, the Dorylinae, which ranges through the tropics of the Old World and America. Their organized populations represent the ultimate in division of labor. Among each species, different jobs are performed by different "castes," so different looking from each other that they might belong to separate genera or families, whereas in actuality they are all brothers and sisters. The study of the sociology of these ants has attracted the attention of some very able and energetic scientists. They had an important impact, for instance, upon Charles Darwin's thinking about his theory of natural selection. It seems to have been the marvelous adaptations of the army ants of tropical America that gave Darwin an idea that some people have accused him of lacking. That was the concept of natural selection working on *groups* instead of just on *individuals*. Actually, there is plenty of evidence in Darwin's works that he was perfectly aware of group survival advantage as a factor in evolution. And one important source of his understanding of the great scope of the selective process was the army ant colony. He saw that the colony was made up of males and a queen that does nothing but breed, and of workers and soldiers that only work and fight, and are fantastically different in form and size both from each other and from their parents. The problem, of course, is that the workers and soldiers are completely sterile. How can evolution work through these sterile creatures by passing changes in their structure down to succeeding generations if there are no succeeding generations?

IN sum: How could advantageous mutations that produced these efficient but sterile workers and soldiers have been passed on genetically? Nowadays, it seems pretty obvious that the selective process works through the fertile queen and male. *They* are the agencies of natural selection. Their fates are geared to the success of the colony. If the colony produces an efficient kind of worker, it will succeed and produce more of that type of efficient worker. If the workers it produces are not as good, the colony will breed less or not at all. In this sense, the workers and soldiers in a termite colony are like the neck of a giraffe. The neck does not breed, but it does contribute to the survival of the body parts that do, and they breed more—and giraffe necks keep getting more efficiently long.

When I was in Nyasaland years ago, a colonial official told me that in the country around the north end of Lake Nyasa there was a tribe that used the jaws of soldier driver ants to suture wounds. This set up vibrations in my memory, because I had heard and read of the same odd bit of medical ethnozoology in tropical America. In both places the technique is simply to hold together the lips of a wound and apply the jaws of the soldier to the edges of the cut. The ant bites, the surgeon breaks off its abdomen, and a section of the gap is clamped shut by the strong, lasting contraction of the jaws, shut first by voluntary contraction of the muscles, then by their drying and hardening. The process is repeated until the whole length of the incision is closed.

Such spectacular examples of convergent ethnic habits incline a man strongly toward the field of anthropology. I had always thought that the way the Indians of southeastern Cuba, the Bajun Island people of the East African coast and some groups in the southwest Pacific had all independently hit on the idea of using sucking fish for catching sea turtles was one of the most fascinating cases of convergence I had heard of. But the ant-jaw sutures seem almost as good, and I wonder why the amazing parallel has not been remarked. Perhaps it has been.

The rain forest is a secret place. It has hidden many of its denizens from the sight of zoologists or has revealed them only piecemeal, through slender tales and elusive clues. The giant forest hog, most imposing member of its family since the Pleistocene, was not discovered until 1904. *Picathartes*, the bizarre, bareheaded rock fowl, was so rarely seen that it seemed out of the world for 80 years following its original discovery. It was not shown in a zoo until 1948. No one knew that there are peacocks in Africa until 1937, when a long epic of almost incredible sleuthing by James P. Chapin proved the existence of a handsome kind of peacock in the Congo forest.

I SUPPOSE the most stirring of the long-kept secrets of the rain forest was the okapi, which inhabits the Ituri forest and the forests about the Semliki River in the upper Congo basin. The okapi became known to zoologists in 1900, more recently than any of the other big land mammals except the giant forest hog. Vague reports had been trickling out for years, heard mostly from the pygmies, but the first solid talk of the existence of a mysterious animal in the upper Congo rain forest was that of the explorer Stanley. His report interested Sir Harry Johnston in the problem, and Johnston's efforts to get at the facts brought out first some scraps of okapi hide, and then at last a whole skin and two skulls. With these, zoologists of the British Museum had all the evidence they needed to be sure that an exciting new animal did indeed live in the Congo rain forest, that it was a kind of giraffe, and that it was dramatically different from the giraffes of the modern earth. The new animal was named after Sir Harry Johnston; it is now known scientifically as *Okapia johnstoni*.

The okapi looks a lot like a short giraffe. The big males stand a little over five feet high at the shoulder, and the back slopes toward the rear, making the forelegs seem longer than the hind legs. In the giraffe, this sloping back changes the mechanics of locomotion, coupling the back muscles in as a part of the driving mechanism for the hind legs. This gives the giraffe a peculiar-looking gait, and this is probably partly shared by the okapi, although few people have ever seen it run. The body is glossy reddish-brown and the face creamy white. The legs are horizontally striped in black and white, the stripes extending high on the rump. The tail is long and tufted. On the forehead is a pair of hornlike projections which are covered by hair nearly to the tips. These begin as swellings in the skin and, as the horns of giraffes do, gradually grow down and fuse with the head bone.

Okapis have in recent years become widely spread among the zoos of the world. There is even an albino okapi in a Belgian zoo. But little is known about their habits in the wild. Like giraffes, they are mainly browsers, eaters of leaves, as one would expect from their forest habitat. Although the lower levels of the rain forest are open and only sparsely set with shrubs and small trees, there is plenty of forage for a solitary browser like the okapi, particularly in the occasional natural openings where low vegetation flourishes for a brief moment in the successional processes that build the forest back again after a stream bank caves in or a big tree falls. Because it stays out of sight of man so thoroughly, I judge the okapi to be in no immediate danger of serious depletion. But its span of life as a natural species will probably not outlast that of the Congo rain forest.

I have until lately never been able to distinguish clearly between my image of the okapi and my even more nebulous concept of the bongo. Both are secretive, both are forest-dwelling ungulates, both are or have been little known to

A MOST USEFUL TONGUE

With its 14-inch-long tongue, the okapi washes out its ears (above), flicks flies from its withers, cleans its face and reaches the tender shoots of many shrubs and trees. The plum-colored tongue is only four inches shorter than that of the much bigger, closely related giraffe. Its prehensility enables the okapi to grasp and pull down branches (below), strip away leaves and pop them into its mouth.

the zoo-going public. The okapi is a relative of the giraffe, while the bongo is a kind of antelope; but in my mind they were confused until I set out to write this book. Now I see why. There is a similar aura about them. The aura is one of mystery. The mystery is made partly by the mysterious way people speak of them, partly by their retiring habits and partly by their spooky looks. Also, both are big, hoofed animals, both live in the forest, and both are obliteratively colored by stripes. The bongo has used the sort of stripes his ancestors had available—the vertical ones of the kudu family. The okapi uses horizontal stripes. Unless there is some difference in the amount or quality of light present in the rain-forest habitat of the okapi and in the montane habitat of the bongo, stripes running differently in the two animals must just show that it is breaking the bulk of the body pattern that is the important thing, and that this is done equally well by vertical and horizontal stripes. Spots will even work, as the leopard and jaguar show.

As habitat for man, no kind of country in all of Africa—not even excepting the howling desert—has been so little lived in as the rain forest. The only human beings who have joined its ecosystem are the Mbuti pygmies. The lives of the Mbuti, by both evolution and cultural adjustment, have been woven into the fundamental web of the forest, and they are now as much a part of it as the colobus monkeys in the trees or the termites in the ground.

There are about 40,000 of the Mbuti people. They live in an area of some 100,000 square miles of the Ituri forest of the eastern Congo. They are hunters and gatherers to whom the primeval forest is the source of life and not a hostile place to be destroyed for safety's sake or to make way for a garden. With bow and arrow or nets, the men hunt the small forest antelope or sometimes bigger game such as okapi and even elephants. They search out smaller game too—ants, termites, grubs and snails—and the women round out the diet with berries, nuts, roots and mushrooms found in the forest.

This way of living keeps the pygmies on the move. They live in camps instead of in fixed villages and think nothing of changing the location of their little settlements at a moment's notice. Their huts are built quickly, being only a tied framework of poles thatched with big leaves of phrynium. They are dry and comfortable, however, and as appropriate to the conditions of the rain forest as a squirrel nest above them in a tree.

Colin Turnbull has written an engrossing book about these little men, whom he knows as well as anyone does. In telling of them in a more recent article, Turnbull reveals his misgivings over the outlook for their future: "The major problem . . .," he says, "is that when it becomes necessary to . . . exploit the forest, what is to become of its inhabitants? Physiologically the Mbuti are ill adapted to life outside the forest, dying quickly of sunstroke and of stomach disorders, and psychologically they are equally handicapped, all their values and beliefs being associated with the forest and their nomadic way of life. . . . Given time the Mbuti would find a way to adapt, but there is not likely to be much time."

That is a sad last phrase of Turnbull's: ". . . not likely to be much time." With more time, men outside the forest might somehow learn to abate their aimless breeding and keep such treasures as the Mbuti on in an unruined Ituri. But the time, as Turnbull says, is running out. The rain forest stands in the way of the spread of the bigger people. The pygmies seem no more likely to last than the rest of the natural world.

THE RED RIVER HOG ROOTS OVER THE FOREST BOTTOM LIKE A PLOW. SEEDS TAKE HOLD QUICKLY IN THE UPTURNED EARTH IT LEAVES BEHIND

Hothouse Animals

Tropic heat and constant moisture produce rain forest—a dense, evergreen umbrella. Trees and vines, seeking sunlight, grapple over a dank and gloomy subregion where dwell the furtive okapi, civet and forest hog. In the canopy above, birds and monkeys are more obtrusive, while from taproot to topmost bud, the whole vegetable entanglement is ceaselessly assaulted by avid hordes of insects.

THE AFRICAN CIVET, a viverrid that can spray an enemy with blinding musk, is, like the skunk, strikingly marked so as to be remembered and avoided. Nose to tail, it measures four feet.

THE GENET is swifter and more aggressive than its cousins the civets. An effortless climber, it cruises along limbs at night seeking live meat, and by day curls up in the hollow of a tree.

On the Ground, Great Stealth

A man can walk for days through the tropical rain forest of Africa without spotting game of any kind on the ground. Yet it exists, not in large herds as it does on the plains of Serengeti, but in surprising numbers nonetheless. Except for birds and monkeys, the larger forest animals are solitary, shy and most often nocturnal. The okapi (*right*), the great forest hog and a species of antelope, the bongo, are the largest. Though described by natives, these three were considered no more than myths until the close of the 19th Century. New species of smaller animals—rats, mice and the like—are being identified every year.

Leopards, which hunt in the deep forest, are not, strictly speaking, at home there. They are native to the forest fringe, as is one of their prey, the red river hog, shown on page 121. The true deep-forest carnivores are the small viverrids, including several species of genets and civets. Their behavior in the wild is little known, as it takes luck, patience and a strong flashlight to get even a glimpse of one. However, the civet's ability to secrete musk is well known. For centuries, civets have been cultivated for this substance, which is used as a perfume base.

A CONGO TRIBUTARY, the Luki River, splits the otherwise solid canopy of the forest, allowing sunlight in. The result is an impassable tangle of undergrowth, unusual on the forest floor.

TWO OKAPIS stand in a forest clearing, their funnel-like ears cocked forward. These wary relatives of the giraffe created a zoological sensation in 1900 when they were first discovered.

MATCHING the pattern of leaves behind it, a scaly pangolin winds around a limb. An African version of the anteater, it uses its prehensile tail as an anchor while clawing open arboreal termite nests.

SQUATTING on a liana, with wings hunched, is a casqued hornbill, named for the growth on its beak. This black-and-white bird, common in the forest, hops from perch to perch more often than it flies.

In the Trees, Strange Shapes

Though far from conspicuous, great numbers of vertebrates live in the trees of the African rain forest. Birds are the most numerous. The casqued hornbill (*left*) has 44 cousins in the Old World tropics. Each has a unique call. The casqued brays like a donkey—others honk, toot, squeal or whistle. Hornbills have the exuberant habit of tossing fruit and insects in the air a few times before swallowing them. Everything goes down whole, the indigestible parts being regurgitated later.

Among treetop mammals, which include mice,

squirrels and primates of all kinds, the most unusual are the pangolins. One large species lives on the ground, but most are arboreal. The pangolin above measures 30 inches overall, 15 of which are tail. It makes an exclusive diet of tree termites and ants, and seldom descends to the ground, since its long claws make normal walking difficult. Plated on back and sides with sharp horny scales, this pangolin has a belly of white fur. Pangolins lack teeth and in defense roll up into a ball. In extremities, they may eject a smell that rivals that of a skunk.

MUD CHEVRONS plastered on a tree by termites act as gutters to deflect rain from a nest at the bottom. Without gutters, the nest might be washed away by rain pouring down the trunk.

ABANDONED by its builders, a huge termitarium, hollowed out and fitted with a door, serves as a storage shed. It did not take long for plants to root once the hard shell went unattended.

For Termites, Dark Forts

One might expect the accumulation of dead vegetable matter on the floor of the rain forest to be immense. However, the microscopic agents of decay work even more intensely than the plants shed, with the result that there is far less debris than there is in the deciduous forest of the Temperate Zone. Much of this rapid return of vegetation to the soil is accomplished by termites—the most prevalent of the forest insects. Unseen, laboring endlessly in the centers of rotting trees and under the carpet of fallen leaves, they chew away at the woody fabric of the forest.

At first it is hard to imagine a creature more poorly adapted to life on earth than the typical termite. Blind, slow, weak, with a soft skin, unable to stand sunlight or changes in temperature or humidity, it nevertheless survives floods, droughts, ants and other prowling insect predators by enclosing itself in a hard-shelled fortress whose walls maintain the internal moisture and even temperature that the termite needs. It builds elaborate tunnels to its sources of food, in order to reduce to a minimum contact with the harsh conditions of the outside world.

ANOTHER DESIGN TO SHED WATER is this nest shaped like a clump of mushrooms. Termites build with a mixture of earth, termite spit and excreta. As this dries, it gets as hard as concrete. Colonies start underground and grow upward, partly to secure better ventilation for their increasing masses, partly to escape the periodic floods which may wipe out young colonies.

Inside the Termite Mound

A termite colony is one of the most intricately organized and efficient societies in the animal world, and its inhabitants the most specialized. When the hard wall of a termite mound is breached, strong-jawed soldiers pour out to defend the nest while smaller workers scurry to repair the damage. Unseen, deep within the mound, are specialists of another kind—the queen and her consort. There, in absolute darkness, protected and imprisoned in a chamber whose exit and entrance are far too small for her to use, the queen lies, swollen, soft and ripe with eggs, the sole reproductive organ of a community which may number millions. The queen in the picture below, accompanied by her male companion and attended by a host of workers, has probably inhabited her cell since the day of her nuptial flight.

At first she looked no different than her consort, but her constant production of eggs has bloated her body out of all proportion. She already may have lain thus for 10 years and may live another five. When she does finally die, the community will not necessarily perish with her. There are substitute queens which can be brought into sexual maturity with proper diet. One of these will then replace her.

©National Geographic

OUT IN THE FIELD, worker termites harvest a fallen leaf. Bit by bit it will be carried inside their mound, mixed with excreta and become the soil for a garden *(below)*.

A FUNGUS GARDEN, which resembles the inside of a walnut, produces tiny white nodules. This is one method termites use to convert cellulose into digestible food.

A TERMITE QUEEN, her head at lower left, lies helpless a moment after her cell is opened. Her consort *(top left)* hides as workers swarm over her distended abdomen.

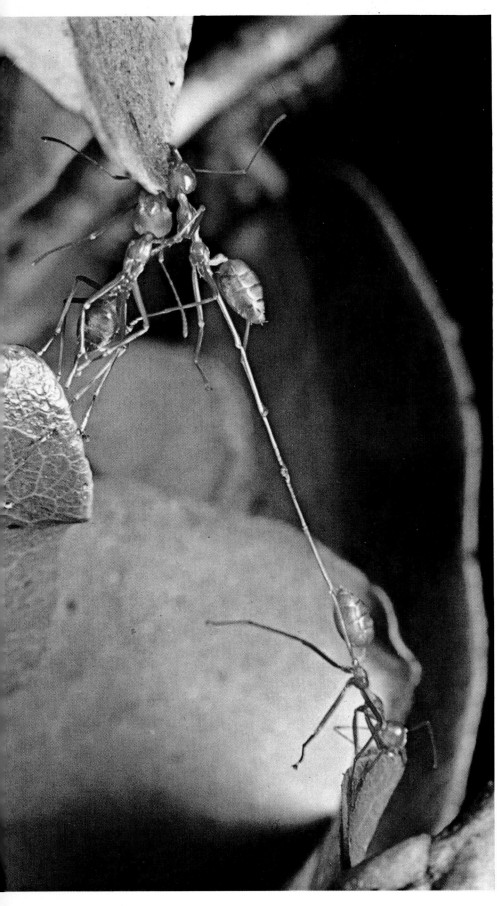

TUGGING IN UNISON, a crew of tailor ants pulls two leaves into position. Joined with webs of fine silk, the leaves will form the walls of the ants' nest. Like worker ants of every species, these are all females.

HIND LEGS LOCKED, two workers forge a thin but remarkably strong chain connecting leaves that are too far apart for one ant. Larger gaps than this are bridged simply by adding more ants to the chain.

For Ants, a Silk-sewn Nest

Tailor ants nest in trees. Not equipped to tunnel in wood, they have evolved a unique system of building. The workers form cocoonlike homes out of living leaves, laboriously pulling them together and then using their own silk-producing larvae as tubes of glue to hold them in place. To do this, the workers take live larvae in their jaws and, squeezing them gently to force out a thread of sticky silk, pass the larvae to and fro like shuttles. Tailor ants are fierce, efficient fighters and tolerate no other insects. A nest cut from one tree and placed in another discourages pests as effectively as modern insecticides.

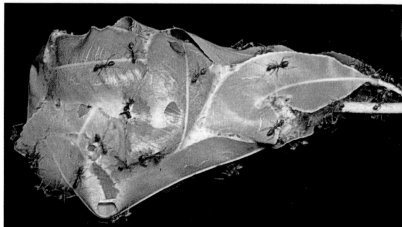

THE FINISHED PRODUCT is a three-inch nest which houses the queen and larvae. The tailor ants on this nest are a different species than the rusty-brown ones in the other two pictures.

The Perplexing Problem of Blue

Tropical regions are the great centers of insect life, and the African rain forest is no exception. Its butterflies are particularly varied and beautiful, and have many things in common with those of South America and tropical Asia—some understandable, some inexplicable. The butterfly below, for example, is a brilliant metallic blue; it shares this striking color with species found in the Amazon and Malaya, but all three are unrelated. There are blue butterflies in cold places too, of course, but most of them are pale or powdery in tint. Deep metallic blue tends to be a phenomenon of the tropics, although no one knows quite why.

One explanation, not so much for blue as for all the bright colors and bizarre shapes of the rain forest, may have to do with the pace of evolution there. In an environment that is warm and humid the year round, some of the danaid butterflies complete their life cycles in less than a month and may get in as many as 10 generations a year, whereas related species in North America have only one. With many niches to evolve into, and rapid evolutionary development a possibility, it is not surprising that the variety of tropical butterflies is as great as it is. Given time, almost any shape or color is theoretically possible, so long as it is not harmful to its bearer.

A METALLIC-BLUE BUTTERFLY, of the genus *Deudorix*, is found in the rain forest of West Africa. The morphoes of South America have this same color, as do some of the nymphalids of Burma and Malaya.

FIVE DIFFERENT SPECIES of butterflies gather at one small Congo mud puddle. Butterflies the world over congregate on mud, but there are fewer kinds in temperate climates and hence less varied congregations.

A FEMALE GORILLA thumps her chest at the approach of a photographer in her mountain home in the eastern Congo. This action, more typical of males than females, is often used to intimidate enemies. It helped establish the long-held opinion that gorillas are ferocious animals. Actually they are inoffensive and harmless unless molested.

6

Islands in the Clouds

ALL through the tropical world, the life of high mountains has an oddly similar look. This is not brought about by current traffic among the mountains. On the contrary, they are as isolated from one another as islands in an ocean. In Africa some of the mountains of the Congo have rain forest around their bases, while others, like Kenya, Kilimanjaro and the Aberdares, stand in dry savanna. In every case the country that separates the mountains from each other is, for many of the creatures that live on them, as effective a barrier as so much salt water would be. For these specially adapted animals of the montane forests and moors, their mountain habitats are islands in the clouds.

There are notable differences among the world's tropical mountain communities, but it is the worldwide similarity in their architecture that first strikes the traveler who visits them. From the lower slopes to the zone at which vegetation disappears, there is a fairly regular, predictable sequence of communities as altitude increases. The rise of the slopes usually wrings increased rain out of the winds that hit them, and a so-called montane rain forest develops. At lower levels this is not greatly different from lowland rain forest in structure. A little higher, however, the rainfall becomes less regular, and the vegetation begins to change. The trees are lower, leaves are smaller, the trunks and limbs are less straight. Lianas, one of the essential marks of the lowland evergreen forest, become fewer, while epiphytic mosses, ferns and other plants grow prodigiously, often completely covering the limbs and twigs, or, as in the case of the hoary old-man's beard, *Usnea*, hanging in festoons from all the branches. Another characteristic mark of the tropical mountain forests is tree ferns, certain species of which may grow to heights of 30 feet or more in protected places. Still another usual component is bamboo. Probably the most widespread tree in the cloud forests of the world is the broad-leafed conifer known as yellowwood.

On some of the tropical African mountains—the Ruwenzori range, for instance, and the Virunga Volcanoes—rain, drizzle, mist or rime are copious and regular. Nearer the Indian Ocean coast, however, on Kenya, Meru and Kilimanjaro, the heaviest rainfall occurs far down the sides of the mountains, and the upper zones may undergo strong seasonal desiccation. On the heights of Kilimanjaro, precipitation may be as little as four inches a year. It is on these drier mountains from Kenya to Malawi that a visitor from tropical America sees the most impressive similarities between the African montane zones and those back home. The resemblances are due mainly to the operation of a comparable set of environmental influences, which tends to mold even wholly unrelated sets of organisms into a similar look. This kind of similarity between communities built of different biologic materials can be spoken of—with due caution, of course—as ecological equivalence.

It is in the higher zones of these drier mountains that African and American mountain communities seem most surprisingly alike. As the timber line is approached, the trees are small and moss-draped, often wind-pruned, and fewer in species. They get an old, underprivileged, wizened look to them, like Japanese dwarfed trees. Nobody seems to know whether the elfin high-mountain trees of tropical East Africa are actually very old, but ring counts have been made in the dwarf forests of Caribbean mountains showing that trees only an inch or so in stem diameter were over 400 years of age.

Related to huckleberries and other humble ericaceous shrubs, the huge tree heaths, some of them 30 feet tall, are one of the curiosities of the African cloud forests. On Kilimanjaro, the main trail leading up to the summit on the eastern side goes through a grand old forest of giant heaths. The trees close high overhead in a woods so suggestive of some kind of conifer that you have to stop and look closely at the leaves to see that they are not.

On all the equatorial mountains of Africa, frost begins to occur at levels from 9,000 to 11,000 feet, and it is here that the vegetation starts to get its "Jack-and-the-beanstalk" look, as Sir Harry Johnston called it, with mossy scrub alternating with glades in which the ground is covered with *Lycopodium*, or set with great senecios and huge postlike lobelias. Above 12,000 feet such plants as *Alchemilla*, everlasting and *Hypericum* give the landscape a strong alpine flavor to match its alpine feel.

One of the southernmost African mountains with a typical mid-African montane community is Mlanje, a bull of a massif standing alone in the dry country of Malawi, south of Lake Nyasa. I once climbed up on Mlanje and spent a night in a foresters' camp on the Chambe Plateau just under the ponderous gray rise of the bare, magnificent peak. It was cold and very dry when I climbed the mountain. The vegetation of the lower slopes began to take on the look of cloud forest at about 4,500 feet. Just before dark I came out on the moorland, an undulating plain of grass where fat-stemmed tree ferns, some of them eight or 10 feet high, stood about like giant toadstools.

I slept under three blankets, before a huge cypress-wood fire. The next morning I walked about the edges of the moors. It was the heart of the dry season, and the mist-famine was obviously severe, the ground powdery except in the deepest ravines. The shrubs and herbaceous plants were already wilting at 10 in the morning. The tree ferns were all crisp brown, evidently hit by frost as well as drought. It seemed to me they could never possibly recover from such a setback, and yet they obviously do—they looked tremendously old.

On that trip I climbed into the high forest, as I said, from a dry landscape. A month later I returned and went part way up the mountain again, this time going through the rain forest that covers the southern approaches, where there had been 131 inches of rain the year before. The climb was short, from 2,500 to about 5,000 feet, but in that slight rise, the change from rain forest to cloud forest was striking. The leaf mold down in the lower woods was wet and almost sloppy to walk through. And yet only a thousand feet higher, where the look of montane forest began, the delicate *Selaginella* and filmy ferns were all curled crisp, and the few tender vascular plants there had wilted. In the low forest it had rained every day for a week before. Up above there was no sign of recent rain at all, not even of condensation of mist or fog.

A HIGH forest in the tropical mountains must live on a water ration that, for part of the year at least, comes mostly as mist and be able to survive in the times when the mist fails to come. Like the resurrection fern that covers the tops of the long lateral limbs of live oak trees and thatches over shingle roofs in rural Florida, it must be ready to come to life in a hurry when the wet comes back. One day the resurrection fern may look as dry as autumn leaves, all curled into hard and wholly lifeless-looking knots. Then it rains in the night, and the next morning all the little fern fronds are standing clean, green and able-looking, as if all their lives had been passed in a greenhouse. It is the same in the high moss forests of the Caribbean, and from the look of Mlanje it must be the same there. How cells can do this I am not enough of a physiologist to tell.

It is probably this drastic fluctuation in moisture, plus lowered temperatures, that makes cloud forest so poorly populated by most animal groups. There is a rule of thumb that the diversity of mountain fauna decreases with increasing altitude. This was demonstrated in the montane rain forest on the lower slopes of Mount Rugege in Ruanda, where Kai Curry-Lindahl and Maxime Lamotte found a fauna much richer than that in the higher montane communities. In only four days and within an area over twice the size of a tennis court, they collected 628 frogs of 11 different species. I doubt that any such concentration of frogs would ever be found higher up in a moss forest or at high levels on the mountains of Kenya and Tanganyika. For amphibians, insects and most other small animals, the danger of desiccation and cold is too great to be tolerated. Because these smaller creatures are scarce, there is little opportunity for insectivores and other meat eaters, and they are scarce too.

Montane forest communities are made up of species that show a curious blend of endemism and convergence. That is, some of the creatures living there are peculiar to (endemic to) their particular high mountain; some may be wholly unrelated types which gradually come to look and behave alike because of environmental influences (convergence). The convergence occurs through the evolutionary molding of the different animals into more or less standard "moun-

A "HAIRY" FROG

What looks like hair on this frog from the Cameroons is actually fine filaments of skin containing a great many small blood vessels which are believed to be an aid in breathing. The frog lives in mountain streams with a high oxygen content, and the hairs, which number about 2,500, more than double the frog's skin surface and thus increase the amount of oxygen that can be absorbed by the skin. The female has no hair. She lives on land and joins her mate in the water only during the breeding season.

A SLOW-GROWING SENECIO

On the cloud-covered heights of Mount Kenya is found the mountain senecio. Because of low temperatures and high humidity there, it grows very slowly, starting life as a low rosette of leaves (first drawing). After about 30 years a three-foot woody shoot emerges from the center of the rosette, covered with the plant's first blossoms. After these flowers die, one or two side stalks will form rosettes of their own, leading to the branched appearance of the mature plant (bottom), which may be 200 years old.

tain forest" shapes, whatever the original shapes of those animals may have been. Endemism can be explained in two ways. Some endemics are ancient relict stocks that were once widespread but have died out everywhere except in the regions in question—on one or a few high mountains, for example. Another kind of endemism is the result of isolation of a stock—in a mountain fastness, say—long enough for it to have evolved into a new form.

Both convergence and endemism are practically inevitable on islands—be they in the sea or in the clouds. What is harder to explain is that in a single area, such as tropical Africa, widely separated mountain environments should contain animals and plants obviously very closely related to each other but never seen anywhere in the territory that separates the mountains. The problem is to explain how they got from one mountain to another. How did the members of each mountain forest community—the animals and plants that give the place its special stamp—come to be where they are? How did they spread to the separate mountains? Could it have been by flying, walking or being blown from one peak to another? To some slight degree, where the heights stand close to each other, or in the cases of certain small, light insects or spiders, seeds or spores, this has surely occurred. But the important puzzle is to explain the seeding of widely separated mountains with kinds of animals that never show up in the intervening areas, animals so adapted to the montane community that they are unable to survive in, or even to travel across, the lowlands in between.

IN desperation for an answer to this question, one might suggest that the montane species evolved separately on each separate mountain. Maybe animals and plants out of the surrounding landscape simply moved up onto the mountains, underwent evolution there and were slowly converted into well-adapted members of an integrated biological community. The similarities among the separate mountain biotas, then, would be similarities due to convergent evolution, to the forcing of creatures into a common mold by a similar set of living conditions. The odd thing about this preposterous-sounding theory is that it is partly true. This is the convergent evolution that I referred to above as one feature of the cloud-forest community.

But how about the species that not only look alike but are closely related also? How do they come to be living in such distantly separated places? The only logical way to account for their distribution is to suppose that the kind of environment they occupy once spread in continuous tracts over broad areas. The intervening landscape is today so different and alien-looking that such a history is hard to imagine. Nevertheless it is the only respectable theory that can account for the facts.

The birds of African mountains have been carefully studied by R. E. Moreau of Oxford, and his work has shed much light on the probable history of the montane communities of the continent. In a recent paper he gives some figures to show the similarities in the faunas of the separate mountains. On peaks around the southern end of Lake Nyasa, 29 of the 33 species of mountain birds found there turn up again in the Usambara Mountains, 700 miles to the north across largely uninhabitable terrain. An even more impressive example of kinship is shown by birds of Cameroon Mountain, which has 41 species not found in the surrounding lowlands; of these, 20 occur again in mountains 1,300 miles to the east. Such sharing of species can mean only one thing. In Moreau's words: "These ecological islands, however widely separated, were colonized by an already integrated community, rather than by a process of random dispersal, as in oceanic islands." Because each of the species involved has refined adjustments to a special kind of environment, the problem is, really, to account for the distribution of the environment. For this, we must assume that there have been climatic changes, and that some of them have been recent. Otherwise, speciation would have brought about greater differences among the birds.

Moreau believes that the conditions required for a great extension of mountain forest from northern Kenya down to Malawi and across to Angola and the Cameroons may have existed as late as 18,000 years ago. His belief is supported by the findings of the pollen expert E. M. van Zinderen Bakker, who in 12 different places in Africa has found fossilized pollen grains from plants which could not have lived under the climatic conditions that exist in those places today. Clearly there has been a shift in climate. It is tempting to link this to the upheavals of the latest ice age which were causing such changes in Europe and North America at about the same time. Van Zinderen Bakker has not been able to find any detailed synchronization between the two, but he has found evidence —through plant distribution—that it was considerably colder in Africa in the Late Pleistocene than it is now. This colder weather would have had the effect of moving the zone of maximum cloud condensation downward on the mountain slopes, which in turn would have meant the joining up of the now isolated mountain forests into large areas of montane vegetation.

Throughout Africa the birds of the cloud forests tend to be unique. And no matter how widely separated, they tend to resemble each other more closely than they do their next-door neighbors at the bottoms of their respective mountains—perhaps only a few miles away. With the mammals this is not the case. Mountain mammals are usually just the more venturesome and ecologically versatile species of the region the mountain is located in. Even up in the moss forests and out on the cheerless moors, there arc mammals; but the species are usually not endemic—not peculiar to mountains at all. They are just able to live there, some permanently, some as casual visitors. There are elephants back of Malindi at sea level, and far up in the bamboos of the Aberdares they snap the tall canes to get at the high browse. Go on above even the bamboo and out into the tangling scrub of heaths and dwarf cedars, and though the landscape seems on the other side of the world from that of the lowlands, it still holds many of the lowland mammals—elephant, buffalo, bushbuck, giant forest hog, eland and even rhino. And wherever such herbivores go, the predators follow. Lions and leopards have been found on most of the East African mountains.

Several kinds of rodents live at high elevations in Africa. There are mole rats on all the equatorial mountains, in the Aberdares and on Mount Kilimanjaro, and I have seen their mounds at the edges of the moors above the upper limit of the forest. One species has been collected at 11,000 feet on Mount Kenya. Living underground would seem a practical plan in the changeable weather of such places. In the benign microclimate of its tunnels, the mole rat no doubt lives more snugly than most other invaders of the alpine levels. There are other small mammals up there, however, that do not burrow. The four-striped grass rat goes up to 10,700 feet or more on Mount Kenya, and the forest mouse occurs in bamboo forests at least that high.

Of all the mammals in the world, the elephant is one of the most wide-ranging in habitat. It roams the highest grasslands of the East African volcanoes, where it has been seen at altitudes of 12,000 feet. Elephants are perfectly at home in any kind of montane vegetation—forest, elfin woodland or moor. They look dis-

A MOUNTAIN HONEY SIPPER

One of the most beautiful of the nectar-sipping African sunbirds is the scarlet-tufted malachite sunbird, which has a long tail, shining metallic-green plumage and a brilliant red breast. It lives in the mountains of East Africa among stands of giant lobelia and senecio, and is seldom seen below 12,000 feet. Sometimes it hovers like a hummingbird as it feeds, sometimes it clings (above). Its long bill is used to sip nectar and to probe for insects beneath the tightly thatched leaves on the lobelia's stalk (below).

concertingly out of place up there, though, as I can say from personal experience.

My encounter with a high-mountain elephant took place in the Aberdares. Three companions and I were quartering the grand, high country in a little English car, looking for animals on the rolling heights and indulging our common predilection for mountain landscapes in tropical lands. All of us had seen such country before, but always somewhere else, never where elephants could conceivably come into the scene. For a while the trip yielded little in terms of animals. A few francolins crossed the road, and some hornbills raved at one another beside it. We saw one squirrel and the last of a troop of proud black-and-white colobus monkeys disappearing in the forest. There were hoofprints of buffalo in plenty on the road, but nothing of the beasts that made them.

The first sign that elephants were on the mountain was some holes we found in the red-brown clay of a road cut. These seemed too conically symmetrical to have been made by road workers' tools, and we stopped to look more closely. Sure enough, the holes in the bank could only be where one elephant after another had poked with his tusks to dislodge cakes of the heavy clay, no doubt to eat for some tonic virtue unknown to us, and perhaps not even known to elephant husbandry. We argued a bit about the holes being maybe tool marks after all, but then we came upon a huge bolster of elephant manure, and that made further argument pointless.

We got into the car, still pondering the business of clay eating. Then all at once we came upon our elephant. We were climbing a very narrow road scratched out of a steep hillside when we saw him. The hill was rising on one side and on the other side it dropped abruptly beside the outer wheels of the car. We came to a blind curve in the little road, rounded it, and suddenly the narrow way was blocked by the incredible high rise of the elephant's rump. It was a rump all deeply wrinkled, as if the elephant had on too-big trousers. A short, tufted tail swung stiffly below the rump, and a pair of vast ears flapped at the sides, in slow rhythm with the elephant's uphill walk.

THIS was the first time any of us had seen an elephant where getting out of the car was not prohibited by stern local ground rules. I clawed my camera out of a bag, opened the door and got out on the narrow shoulder between the car and the abyss beside it, and tried to focus on the preposterous posterior that so dramatically filled the road ahead. But before I could frame the image, the jog of the curve cut into the form of the elephant and blotted it away. I started to run up the road, not without trepidation but goaded on by the thought of myself photographing a wild elephant on a mountainside. I moved into the bank to keep hidden as long as I could and I ran along beside the wall a little way, and then suddenly the curve ended, the road opened, and I was looking the elephant squarely in the face from only 20 feet away.

I tried to bring the camera up, but quickly thought better of it and bolted. As I ran, my mind shot past the crisis of the instant to the predicament we would be in when the charge of the elephant was blocked by our little car so precariously perched in the scratch on the side of the mountain. For a moment I thought how the only manly thing to do would be to throw myself from the road into the yawning drop beside it and save my friends that way. But I was not up to that and only kept on running. Just before I reached the car, where the irresponsible scorn of my friends showed on their faces through the windshield, I looked back for the indignant bulk of the elephant. It was not there. I stopped and breathed for a second or so, and still no elephant appeared. I got quickly into the car, into the midst of my ignominy, and we started it up and in low gear crept around the curve; and there the elephant was going over the rim of the road cut, crashing down the brushy mountainside, somehow keeping his feet under him all the way to the bottom.

At the foot of the slope, there was a flat, clear swale. When the elephant came out into this he stopped and wheeled. He looked up our way, waved his trunk in the air and made his ears look very big. We took some pictures of him down there in the clearing in the heather. He looks very small and far off in them, though. He is nowhere near the elephant he was, up in front of the Morris Minor on the narrow cliffside road.

O F all the larger mammals, the bongo is one of the most dedicated habitués of mountain forests. To the lucky few who have seen this animal at home, it seems to embody the spirit of the mist forests and high bamboo. It is a member of the bushbuck group, all of which have spirally twisted horns and vertical markings on their sides. The group includes—besides bushbucks proper—the elands, the rare and handsome nyalas and the kudus. The bongo is a large antelope, only a little smaller than the eland. It is reddish brown with white stripes, and the high, twisted horns are found in both the male and the female. Its range extends all the way across the tropical middle of Africa, although it has been reduced by hunting and deforestation. In West Africa the habitat includes open grasslands, but in East Africa the bongo is found only in mountain forests, and there only very sparingly. In Kenya it occurs only on Mount Kenya, in the Aberdares, in the Cherangani range and in the Mau highlands; the recent proclamation of the South West Mau Forest Reserve was aimed mainly at providing another sanctuary for the bongo.

In former times the Kenya bongo made migratory journeys among the highlands, but today it shows little of the old nomadic habit. It is the most elusive, secretive animal of the high forest and nowhere holds up well in contact with man. Its restriction to montane forest in Kenya may have been brought about by the Wandorobo, a tribe of talented hunters who for ages have prized bongo horns for making ceremonial snuff boxes and bugles. Its more recent persecution can be blamed on the Mau Mau emergency. An easily snared animal, it is safest when the materials for making snares are unobtainable. Unfortunately, during the emergency, the Security Forces left wire cable lying all about in the highlands, and this was quickly made into snares by the local Africans. One observer, Venn Fey, found 300 snares on a single hill. In some areas this new pressure has completely eliminated the bongo.

A peculiar reaction of bongos, which probably has contributed heavily to their decline, is their habit of coming to bay in any body of water, however shallow, when chased by dogs. Under most conditions the bongo is excessively wary and almost impossible to approach in the forest. Even the most scrupulously careful approach by expert trackers usually winds up with the creature stampeding out of its bed from a few yards away and denying to the hunter even a glimpse of its ghostly form retreating among the trees. When dogs chase it, however, the attitude of the animal changes. At the first stream crossing, it wheels to face them and is easily killed by the hunters. Where uncontrolled hunting with dogs occurs, there is little hope that the bongo will survive.

As grand a creature as the bongo is, if I had to name the two most exciting species of cloud-forest animals of the world, I think they would be the quetzal of Central America and the African mountain gorilla. Seeing a quetzal in a mist-swept forest is, as I keep saying, a thing to remember forever. While I never saw gorillas in the wild, I have seen George Schaller's stunning pictures of them up in the dwarf forest of moss-smothered rose trees on the Virunga Volcanoes. The look of the vast, shaggy old men up there in the elfin woodland on the cold top of Africa seems to me to be just about the ultimate in zoological things to see.

Like most of the mountain mammals of Africa, the gorilla is not by any means restricted to cloud forest. It shows a good deal of ecological flexibility and is ready to take advantage of the food resources of old fields and clearings. It is nevertheless fundamentally a forest animal. And because gorillas in the wild are wholly herbivorous and eat mainly leaves, the preferred habitat is moist evergreen forest, be this in the lowlands or on the mountains. Schaller and John Emlen found that the mountain race could be watched most easily in the open dwarf forest and in the mountain meadows of giant lobelias and senecios. On the Virunga Volcanoes, they found gorillas living regularly above 11,500 feet and sometimes reaching elevations of 13,500 feet.

THE differences among the cloud forests of the world are one of their arresting qualities—there being in some of them gorillas and in others quetzals. But a more mystic marvel of these islands in the clouds is, as I have said, the almost uncanny sameness. To bring back the feel of this sameness to my mind, nothing serves better than thinking of the fluted notes of the thrushes in cloud forests everywhere, the jilguero of the mainland tropics of America, the long-day-bird in Jamaica, and in Africa the to-me-unknown kinds of thrushes that make the same sounds in all the dim forests of the mountains there. I have spoken of this to various friends and all show clearly they think I am pretty unreliable to talk of such a thing. But I can't help trying to think of some way in which the fluid character of the African and American thrush songs might be not just proof of common heredity but in some way also an adaptation to life in a high mist forest. This is a fairly silly thought, but all the same, I wish I could go back with witnesses to a place I know up the Likubula trail on Mlanje Mountain. There is a little stream there near the edge of the plateau where a stand of tree ferns leans over the purling water, and a big gnarled yellowwood rises over them, its branches waving moss in the slow breeze of the waning afternoon. A shiny lizard runs around the base of the yellowwood, a brown frog sits beside a pool in the rill, you lean out over the pool and little crabs scurry back beneath the undercut banks at the sight of you. A wisp of the evening fog drifts into the glade, and after it there comes, incredibly floating on the cool air, floating in from 8,000 miles away, the golden notes of the jilguero.

It is not really the jilguero singing, of course. But it is another kind of thrush so precisely able to fill the same scene with the same magic sound that you fairly forget to breathe. To show exactly what I mean I will somehow have to move with the witnesses I spoke of to another high glen, on a mountain in Honduras, up under the spire of El Volcán. Because it will all be up there again, all just the same: the yellowwood tree with the million mosses on its twisted limbs, the tree ferns over the cold brook, the shiny lizard, the brown frog on the bank, the little crabs in the pool scurrying in the same terror. And if the hour and the time of season should be the same, a wisp of mist will float through the woods, and again the jilguero will sing, up there 8,000 miles away from the little crabs in the pool on Mlanje Mountain.

HEATHS, WHICH IN NORTHERN LANDS GROW NO HIGHER THAN A MAN'S THIGH, ON THE SLOPES OF KILIMANJARO MAY REACH UP TO 26 FEET

Highland Greenery

Unlike most tropical mountains—the Andes, for instance—Africa's mountains are not linked together. Some capped by ice, they rise from rain forest or dry plains to form biotic islands. Despite this, their flora, though abounding in unique species, looks remarkably like that of other tropical mountains. Even the bizarre senecios and giant heaths (above) have their counterparts in other lands.

143

KILIMANJARO, the continent's highest mountain, looms out of the early morning mist above the dry *Acacia* plains of East Africa. Its icecap is receding, no one knows why, leaving a cold, barren belt of volcanic rock and sand, seen just above the clouds. There, rain and melt water are absorbed at once, appearing as springs lower on the mountain. The only vegetation is moss and lichen. Hidden behind the clouds, which will build above the summit as the day lengthens, the green belts begin—first, sparse grasses, scattered shrubs and tree senecios, then, lower down, the zone of giant heath pictured on the previous page. Below that, where most of the rain falls, grows the thick montane forest, much of it replaced by crops.

145

Blooms on Mountain Flanks

The mountain forest belts, up to 8,000 feet, make far better showcases for Africa's wild flowers than do the lowland rain forests. Both regions produce blooms the year round, but on the mountain sides the blooms are visible to the eye, whereas in the rain forest they are up in the canopy where the sunlight is and are virtually hidden to anyone standing on the ground.

The typical nonwoody flower in the lowland rain forest is an epiphyte perched on a branch high above the dark forest floor and taking its moisture and nourishment from the air. Although the mountains may be just as rainy as the rain forest below, the climate is cooler. As a result the trees are smaller and grow farther apart. Sun filters through, and herbaceous plants like those shown on these pages are able to produce blossoms on or near the ground. Even orchids, most of whose tropical species are epiphytes, adhere to this rule. In the highlands and above they are increasingly found growing rooted in the soil, like the knee-high one shown at the left.

TWO SPIKY BLOSSOMS belong to different forest belts. The lusher, yellow one, harboring a beetle, does not grow above 3,000 feet, whereas the pink one is found only above 6,500.

A RARE ORCHID, *Disa erubescens*, is found growing at 5,000 feet in swampy highlands in Burundi. The color range of the handsome species varies from scarlet all the way to albino.

TOUCH-ME-NOT grows in damp, shady places. Its seedpods burst when ripe, throwing seeds over a wide radius. Touching the plant often triggers these tiny explosions, hence the name.

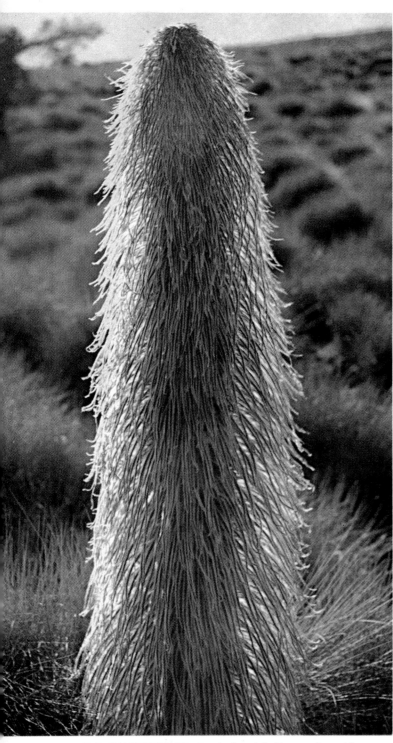

THE SHAGGY PILLAR of a six-foot lobelia stands amidst dry tussocks. Its hairy foliage protects it against the cold and drought high on Mount Kenya's moorland girdle.

UNDER A FRESH FALL OF SNOW, tree senecios tower over a climber on Mount Ruwenzori. These plants grow just below the glacier line on Africa's mountains and often reach heights of 15 feet or more. They are closely related to an American weed, the groundsel, well known to most farmers and rarely getting more than a foot high.

THE RUFFED LEMUR, one of 20 species found only on Madagascar, is a nocturnal tree dweller. With the coming of dawn, it draws itself up, stretches out its arms and faces the sun, a habit that has made it sacred to some of the Malagasy people.

7

The Naturalist's Promised Land

A BOOK on African natural history might reasonably be expected to limit its scope to the African continent proper. There are certainly plenty of animals there to write about. But no zoologist worth his salt could get that close to the great island of Madagascar without saying at least a little about that vast, fantastic land with a fauna so extraordinary that it has evoked for itself the name Promised Land of the Naturalist.

Madagascar, the Malagasy Republic as it nowadays is called, is located in the western Indian Ocean, off the coast of East Africa. Its northern end lies about 12 degrees south of the equator, and the island is some 1,000 miles long, with a greatest width of about 360 miles. At the nearest point, the mainland is 244 miles away across the Mozambique Channel. Compared to the 240,000-square-mile area of Madagascar, this water gap seems narrow, but it is a very old, stable one and is more than 3,000 feet deep over a broad zone through its entire length. Although some evidence suggests the channel may have been narrower in the past, the make-up of the present fauna gives no sure sign of any land connections during the past 60 million years. Dinosaurs occur as fossils in the sedimentary rocks of the island, but no one is sure when the land they may have crossed on existed, or even whether they came in overland at all. Philip Darlington thinks there may have been no land connections to Madagascar since the Triassic. In any case, a long isolation by a salt-water barrier is the key to the almost unequaled zoogeographic interest of the Madagascar fauna.

The central part of the island is a long plateau mostly 3,000 to 5,000 feet above sea level, with scattered peaks rising above 9,000 feet. Over much of this area, and along the coasts as well, the vegetation has been drastically changed by man. Along the east coast a palm pandanus strand and marshy lowlands and lagoons give way to woods that grow increasingly lush as the land rises and becomes a closed-canopy forest along the eastern highlands. This forest evidently was once continuous, but now is much reduced. The whole central plateau is today a grassland, highly modified by fire and grazing, and with trees only where they have been planted about the towns, or where reforestation has taken place or firewood coppices established. The western part of the island, once mostly deciduous forest, is now almost all dry steppe-savanna. The southernmost tip of the island is scrub country in which numerous endemic desert plants make a bizarre flora of great botanical interest, but which is being fast diminished by the constant burning the region undergoes.

Considering only the lay of the land itself, there are several different histories one might think up for an island like Madagascar. It might have come up from the floor of the sea, full-blown as an island. Or it might not always have been an island, but been cut off by rising seas from some larger mass of neighboring land. In the case of Madagascar, the nearest large land masses are Africa, which is close, and India, which is a long way off; so Africa is the choice one would lean to on purely geographic grounds.

We postulate, then, that Madagascar was cut off from Africa, and then we look about for ways to test this notion. The most conclusive way would be to find continuous strata of rock running from Madagascar, under the Mozambique Channel, and appearing again on the African mainland. Unfortunately, as in most such cases, this kind of straightforward stratigraphic proof cannot be found. The other alternative is to seek evidence among the animals and plants that are living there now. Madagascar has one of the most distinctive faunas in the entire world, with features that shed a little light upon the ways and times of their recruitments.

Fᴿᴼᴹ the standpoint of zoogeography, there are two kinds of islands in the seas of the earth: continental islands and oceanic islands. A continental island is one that lies near a big adjacent land and has received its fauna from it. The animals of the island therefore resemble those of the neighboring land, even though they now may be living in complete isolation.

Oceanic islands get their animals by accidental distribution. Arising from the bottom of the sea, they have no history of connection with places in which there are old, organized, balanced faunas, and so their biological communities are pieced out fortuitously. This usually means by waifs that blow or drift in with winds or current, or fly in on strong wings, or by creatures converted by evolution from marine forms that invaded the land edge. The result of such a process of recruitment is a taxonomically uneven fauna which any zoogeographer can recognize at a glance. Many types, like the fresh-water fishes and amphibians, will be very poorly represented. But there will be a disproportionate representation of aerial species such as birds and insects.

Through the eons of evolutionary time, the ways of making a living have been exploited—adopted, refined and subdivided—by special groups that have become more or less committed to certain basic specialties and can be expected to turn up in those roles in any part of the earth. Wherever there are trees, for instance, woodpeckers can be expected, and most of the world's woodpeckers are members of an interrelated group, a taxonomic family that long ago got committed to pecking wood. In oceanic islands one finds a contradiction of this rule. The island niches may seem to be quite variously exploited, but look closely and the exploiters of them turn out not to be the expected bloodlines. There may be birds pecking at the trees all right, but they are not woodpeckers. There may be squirrels in the trees that are not even rodents, or fish in the streams that are not kin to any other fresh-water fishes anywhere else, but have their closest relatives in the adjacent sea. That is what is meant by a disharmonious fauna. Its main features are fewness of, and irregular representation by, taxonomic groups, and makeshift exploitation of ecological roles.

Madagascar confounds the zoogeographer with signs that suggest both land connections and long isolation. In some ways it is a good clear example of an oceanic island—a big one to be sure, but still a separate and aberrantly populated region with features very different from those of the nearest continent. Africa, being the nearest continent, is the land mass to which one should look for the greatest similarity in fauna. And sure enough, if one compares Madagascar animals with those of the rest of the world, the relationships with Africa turn out to be far more clear-cut than with India, the next nearest place.

THE most stirring element in the strange Madagascar fauna is its lemurs. Lemurs are among the most primitive of the primates, which in a general way puts them close to the common ancestors of monkeys, apes and men. Most people, hearing that lemurs are prosimians and having seen them only as textbook figures, dismiss them as an inferior sort of primate, an only half-formed, unworthy kind of monkey. This is a mistake. Over and above their abounding scientific interest, lemurs are a pleasant, versatile and well-adjusted lot of creatures that anybody ought to be happy to be descended from.

Madagascar has three endemic families of lemurs, made up of 10 genera and more than twice that many species. Fossils show that only a short while ago they were a good deal more diverse. There was, for example, a terrestrial lemur the size of a calf, with huge canine teeth like a baboon's. It padded through the Pleistocene of Madagascar, contemporaneous with giant, ostrichlike, flightless birds and huge tortoises, both also extinct.

There are lemur types of a slightly different kind in Africa and Asia. This led early zoogeographers to theorize that Madagascar is all that is left of a land mass that connected Africa and India during relatively recent—Cenozoic—times. They gave the land the name Lemuria. Unfortunately for this notion, fossil lemurs later turned up in Europe and America too. Some 60 million years ago, little lemurlike primates spread through much of the northern lands that now constitute North America and Eurasia. Later on, the separation of the continents segregated the stocks, and they evolved an abundance of different types. Still later, extinction overtook most of the world's lemurs, leaving them only in Africa, southwestern Asia and Madagascar, where we find them today. This is, of course, a vast oversimplification of lemur history. It leaves nearly 30 million years of their past unaccounted for. But at least we know enough not to concoct a Tertiary continent of Lemuria.

Most students separate the modern lemurs into two groups, lemuroids in

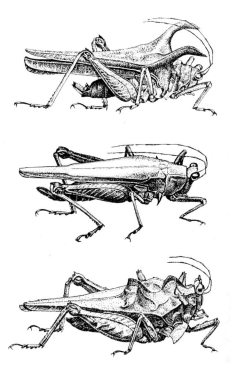

IF YOU LIKE SPIKES . . .

The rain forest of Madagascar supports three very odd grasshoppers. Each has horns, bumps, spikes or other hard protuberances on its body which presumably make it less appetizing to eat than an ordinary grasshopper. Many of the smaller toothless reptiles might have to spit these grasshoppers out and would probably learn in time not to bother them.

Madagascar, and lorisoids in Asia and mainland Africa. The continental ones include some arresting creatures, and something has been said of those in Africa in another chapter. The real headquarters of lemur diversity, though, is Madagascar. The Promised Land of the Naturalist is called that mainly because of the wonderful lemurs there.

What happened to the lemurs in Madagascar is what usually happens to animals, and plants too, for that matter, that find themselves in the sequestered peace of an oceanic island. In the absence of any other enterprising, active arboreal mammal—in the absence, that is, of strong competition—the lemurs proceeded to evolve in ways that adapted them to a great variety of niches in the environment. In filling these roles they of course added to the complexity of the environment, and thus built more niches, and then filled those too. Today there are Malagasy lemurs as small as rats, and others that could stand flat-footed and pull the hat off the head of a tall man.

THE so-called true lemurs belong to the family Lemuridae. Most of them are about the size of a house cat, though a few are much smaller. All have fine, soft fur. Most of the species are forest dwellers. The ring-tailed lemur, however, occupies the dry, nearly treeless section of western Madagascar, where it roams in small bands over somewhat the same kind of bare, rocky terrain that baboon troops frequent on the mainland.

The mouse lemurs are among the smallest living primates, one species having a body length of only five inches. Of all the Madagascar lemurs, they are also the most closely related to the African galagos, or bush babies. All are nocturnal, arboreal and either vegetarian or insectivorous. They run about the trees at night whistling in shrill voices and fighting a great deal. One kind of mouse lemur sometimes occupies the hollows of bee trees; no one knows how it is able to calm the ire of the bees. Mouse lemurs are unusual in their ability to go into a dry-season torpor. Throughout the dry months they remain inactive, rolled into a ball in a leaf nest or in a hollow tree trunk. These periods of seasonally lowered metabolism are comparable to the hibernating of cold-climate animals. They are preceded by intense feeding activity, during which large amounts of fat are stored, especially in the tail and about the rump, just as in mammals preparing for the suspended animation of a hibernation period. This is so pronounced in one form that it is called the fat-tailed lemur.

The most fantastic of all the lemurs is the small, very aberrant and wholly engrossing aye-aye, for which a whole separate family has been established. The only other member of the family is a slightly larger but very similar species known only as a fossil. The aye-aye is a squirrel-like animal, the size of a big cat, with a long bushy tail, big ears and a heavy coat of coarse, dark hair. It has teeth completely unlike those of all other primates and strongly convergent with those of rodents. The incisors are long and chisel-like and are separated from peculiar flat-topped cheek teeth by a wide space. The most distinctive mark of the aye-aye is its freakishly long, slender fingers. The middle one is especially skinny, and looks as meatless and unalive as a dry twig. Although little is known about the habits of aye-ayes, the function of the queer teeth and slim finger are partly understood. Captive aye-ayes have been watched using their finger to make a meticulous toilet, combing and cleaning the whole body, face, coat and tail with the single claw. The finger is also used in drinking—to flip coconut milk or egg yolk into the mouth. Still other and perhaps more fundamental uses are as a prospecting hammer in locating wood-boring insects and as a probe for picking them out. The aye-aye listens for the sound of a worm tunneling a branch, prospects by tapping the surface with its fingernail, then opens the wood with the chiseling incisors and plucks the grub out of its tunnel with its long slender digit. This peculiar finger thus serves some of the functions of the bill and tongue of woodpeckers, and reminds one of the Galápagos finch that plucks a cactus thorn to pick out wood-boring grubs. The woodpecker niche must have strong drawing power. The entering of it by the aye-aye is another beautiful example of convergence.

The largest and most apelike—in appearance at least—of Madagascar lemurs belongs to the family Indriidae, which includes the big, short-tailed indri, the small, round-headed avahi and the varicolored, monkeylike sifaka. Most of the species are diurnal, although the avahi is most active at night. All live mostly in trees, but sometimes they walk about on the ground in an upright position. This striking tendency to a vertical orientation of the body is characteristic of the group. Even when in trees they tend to hold to vertical limbs and to keep the axis of the body vertical also. This gives the indri a more manlike look than that of many primates that are actually much further along in the evolutionary trend toward the humanoid state.

After its spectacular lemurs, which are one of the earth's great zoological treasures, the most noteworthy Madagascar mammals are insectivores. Two of these are shrews, probably accidentally brought in by man. The rest all belong to an odd, endemic family, the Tenrecidae, or tenrecs. The tenrecs are probably more deeply involved in the ecology of Madagascar than any other vertebrates. In the absence of any endemic hedgehogs, moles and mice, and with only a handful of native rats on the island, the family has spread out into a great variety of adaptive niches, not only living like those animals but in some cases looking like them. Certain of the tenrecs, for example, have spiny coats like hedgehogs.

The smallest of the family is the pygmy tenrec. It is about the size of a long-tailed shrew and thus is among the tiniest of living mammals. It lives in burrows in the earth and eats insects. The long-tailed tenrec is not much bigger. Its body is only about two inches in length, but it has a tail five or six inches long with one more vertebra in it than in the tail of any other mammal whose tailbones have been counted. It evidently uses the tail in balancing during the long jumps it makes. Others in the family are the marsh tenrec, with webbed feet, and the rice tenrec, which tunnels in low-lying ground and is common in rice paddies. Altogether some 30 tenrecs are known to science.

THE occurrence of these animals on Madagascar raises another big zoogeographic question, because their nearest kin are thought by some to be a few rare, secretive, little long-nosed insectivores known as solenodons, found in Cuba and Haiti. Their extraordinary distribution would thus parallel that of iguanid lizards, which are known in Madagascar and America but are completely absent from Africa, Asia and Europe. Whatever such peculiar ranges mean cannot be exactly told, but the explanation will not be found in any old lost bridge connecting Madagascar and America while somehow skirting Africa.

Besides lemurs and insectivores, and the few members of the civet-mongoose group, mammals are very sketchily represented in Madagascar. The cosmopolitan house mouse and roof rat are there, and some 16 kinds of native rodents, all belonging to a single subfamily and showing the radiation that one expects to find on islands. There is a sea cow—the East African dugong—in the coastal

A SPECIALIZED FINGER

In addition to grooming its fur with its long, twiglike middle finger, the aye-aye, a rare Malagasy lemur, uses it to flip liquids like egg yolk and coconut milk into its mouth. To eat an egg, the aye-aye first neatly bites off the end, then begins flicking its specialized finger from egg to mouth so fast that the action appears blurred. This continues until the eggshell is empty; not a drop of the yolk is spilled.

waters. The only ungulate, except for recently introduced game species and domestic stock gone wild, is a river pig whose ancestor may have swum the Mozambique Channel, presumably at some time when it was narrower than it is now. This possibility seems strengthened by the occurrence of a Madagascar pygmy hippopotamus, which, though now extinct, did live on the island during the Pliocene and Pleistocene. Its nearest living relative is found in West Africa. The occurrence of these two herbivores—the hippo very aquatic, and the river hog somewhat so—in an island with no recent land connection in its history practically proves the reality of chance dispersal of the ancestors of the two.

Each of the other vertebrate groups reinforces in its own way the picture of Madagascar as an old, isolated island area with no recent land connections in its past. Even among the birds, which in general are less hindered by water barriers than other vertebrates—and thus less useful as geographic indicators—the general picture is borne out. There is an obvious African cast to the birds, more apparent than among the more earthbound forms of life. There is another, less conspicuous bird component that has Oriental kinships. Finally, there is a strong representation of peculiarly Malagasy birds. Among these are some relatives of the ground thrushes known as philepittas, the shrikelike vangas, a lot of endemic rollerlike species, and a group of flightless birds somewhat intermediate between rails and cranes. Two genera of huge, flightless elephant birds are now known only as fossils. Some of them were probably alive when the early Malagasy settlers arrived. A few birds with very close African affinities—a guinea fowl, for example, practically indistinguishable from its African kin—probably represent very recent arrivals, possibly brought in by man.

THREE UNIQUE TREES OF THE ISLANDS

The "coco de mer," or double coconut, is native to the Seychelles but has been introduced elsewhere by man. Its nut is the largest seed in the world and may weigh 40 pounds. It takes six years for this huge fruit to mature; then it falls to the ground and germinates within a year. A tree rarely flowers until it is at least 30 years old, and does not attain its full growth for a century or more.

THERE are no strictly fresh-water fishes in Madagascar. The native fish fauna consists of cichlids and killifishes, both of which are characteristically tolerant of salt water and sea-edge environments, and of species directly derived from marine kinds. In view of the bewildering diversity and richness of the fish fauna of continental Africa, this scarcity seems one of the most notable features of Madagascar zoogeography.

The amphibians of Madagascar are all frogs—some 150 species of them—mostly exclusively Malagasy kinds. One group of 21 species is all probably derived from a single ancestor. The frog pattern follows that of the other animal groups: it has incongruous gaps, strong African and endemic components, and lesser but clear kinships with Asia. Of reptiles, Madagascar has the Nile crocodile and a fair but ragged representation of turtles, snakes and lizards.

The strangeness of the Great Island Madagascar is shared by the other islands of the western Indian Ocean, and in some of these it is even exaggerated—which is to be expected because of their much smaller size. The Mascarenes—Mauritius, Rodriguez and Réunion—lying to the east of Madagascar, and the Seychelles, 600 miles to the north, are all small, volcanic, oceanic islands rising from abyssal ocean. All have markedly ragged endemic faunas, or had them until man came. Like Madagascar, all have undergone the most dismal devastation during the past two or three centuries. On all of them, zoological wonders have been forever blotted out by the heedlessness of man.

The most conspicuous indigenous land animals that the early voyagers found in these islands were giant tortoises—huge, benign, slow-moving vegetarian turtles that reached weights of 500 pounds or more. Each of the islands probably had its own race of tortoise, and in earlier times giant forms lived on Madagascar too. They swarmed in almost unbelievable numbers. Today they are seen only on Aldabra, a small island to the northwest of Madagascar. The cause of this inexorable persecution of big tortoises has been the poor creature's extreme edibility and its amenability to being carried about alive. Like the green turtle, which was also wiped out of much of its primitive range by early voyagers, tortoises keep alive a long time in the hold of a ship, and so provide for a ship's company a lasting supply of fresh meat and a way to prevent scurvy.

But fast as the decline of the giant tortoise was, for speed and thoroughness it failed to match the wasting away of the dodo of Mauritius. The dodo went so early, so fast and so completely that its name has come to serve the language as a metaphor in conjuring up the idea of deadness, obsolescence or goneness—so much so that some people think of the dodo as a beast out of somebody's mythology, like the roc, the phoenix or the unicorn. Actually, the dodo was real enough, and a good likeness appears in James Greenway's book, *Extinct and Vanishing Birds of the World*. What is depicted is the world's strangest bird, a short-legged corpulent creature weighing up to 50 pounds, with degenerate wings, and wholly incapable of flight. The dodo's bill was nine inches long and was black and hooked at the tip. The forehead and face were bare, and the body covered by ashy-gray, hairlike feathers. The tail was a sparse, improbable tuft. Just looking at a dodo, it would be hard to judge what its nearest kin among other birds might be. Ornithologists believe its ancestor was some kind of pigeon that accidentally made its way to the island and, finding plenty of food on the ground and no predators or strong competition to cope with, lost all sense of genetic responsibility and got to be the dodo.

The dodo was first seen by Europeans when the island was discovered in 1507. One hundred and seventy-four years later the last dodo died. Two factors worked to wipe it out: direct depredation by man, and changes in the sequestered environment in which its impractical physique had been allowed to evolve. Because dodos were big, easily caught and fair eating, they attracted ships that were running short of victuals, which ships in those days always seemed to be doing.

Besides the inroads made by mariners, a worse danger soon faced the dodo —predation by the feral livestock and animal stowaways that came in with ships' cargoes. On Mauritius, there soon were rats, cats and pigs, and, by some strange whimsy of the early settlers, macaque monkeys, which eat anything in prodigious quantities and must surely have sought out every dodo egg for miles around. Anyway, all that remains of the dodo is a lot of bones and a pitiful scrabble of other relics, which Greenway inventories thus:

"A great store of bones has been found in a marsh, the Mare-aux-Songes, in Mauritius, and these are in the British Museum, Paris, Leyden, Brussels, Darmstadt, Berlin, and New York. A head and foot are preserved in the Ashmolean Museum at Oxford University. . . . The British Museum possesses a foot, and there is a head in Copenhagen, and a small fragment in Prague." A small fragment in Prague. That really sounds pathetically extinct, doesn't it.

THERE were two other dodolike birds called solitaires in the Mascarenes, and they met fates similar to that of the true dodo. The one on Réunion has left no remains of any kind. It is not even known definitely when it became extinct, although this surely happened before 1800. Contemporary drawings and descriptions indicate that it was much like the Mauritius dodo. Nothing is known of its habits. The other solitaire lived on the neighboring island of Rodriguez. While no skins of this have been saved, great numbers of bones have

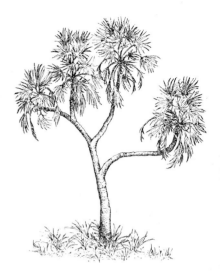

The branched palm is found in Madagascar as well as the Somali coast. It is the only palm with branched stems and is an important tree. Its leaves are woven into ropes, its fruit can be fermented to yield alcohol, and the central kernel of its nut is used in making buttons.

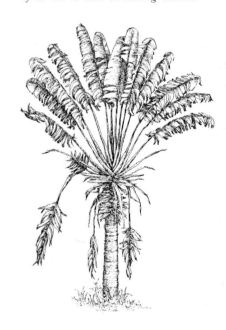

Also native to Madagascar is the traveler's tree, so called because of its water storing capability. The bases of its fan-shaped leaves form a cistern for the collection of rain water, and when this is tapped, as much as a pint of clear liquid will spout from the base of each leaf.

been found in caves and crevices and several skeletons have been reconstructed. This bird had become so rare by 1731 that a naturalist living on the island at that time wrote that he had never seen one.

Besides these great, fat, earthbound pigeons, which showed so graphically the evolutionary effects of excluding competition and predation as selective factors, there were various other flightless birds in the Mascarenes—one or two flightless rails on each island, and flightless herons on Rodriguez and Réunion. All are now gone. In fact, of an original endemic bird fauna estimated at 28 species, 25 are now extinct.

In Madagascar it is not easy to get a clear picture of the original landscapes from the scraps that remain. Human colonization came too early and worked too fast. Even before the advent of Europeans, the Arabs, Malayans and Negroes had come and had brought with them the seeds of destruction—domestic stock, small mammal predators, a demand for timber and fuel wood, the use of fire in pastoralism. The aboriginal Malagasy savannas must have been extraordinarily suitable for grazing, because cattle went wild at an early date and great herds spread throughout the open country in numbers that seem incredible. Some idea of their prevalence is given by accounts of the royal hunts of the Malagasy kings, on which both wild cattle and native game were killed in tremendous numbers. In his book *Three Visits to Madagascar*, published in 1858, William Ellis wrote that hunting wild cattle and wild boars with the spear was the amusement of "daring and adventurous chiefs" of 150 years before his time. The hunting expeditions of King Radama were, according to Ellis, "more like organized military invasions than ordinary pursuits of the chase . . . Radama sometimes led two or three thousand troops to the chase, and, as a portion of these carried fire-arms, the slaughter was immense." On one such expedition 3,063 wild cattle and 2,235 wild fowl were slaughtered, plus numerous wild boars, turtles and monkeys, and a smattering of other animals from crocodiles to tenrecs.

Zoogeographically speaking, the man-made losses in Madagascar and her neighbors represent one of the greatest, per acre, the world has known. To me, the devastation of these amazing islands would not seem quite so bad if we had only kept the dodo. The ruin of the dodo stands as a symbol of mindless destruction. Unless, as some say, early man helped wipe out mammoths, glyptodons, giant sloths and the rest of the Pleistocene savanna fauna, no extinction by human hands can match that of this gross, inept bird. The passenger pigeon was, after all, a pigeon, and the world is full of pigeons. The extinct Carolina parakeet has kin left in the world, and the ivory-billed woodpecker, in slightly different guise, still chops at Central American trees. But nowhere is there anything remotely like the dodo. It was a fantastically vulnerable species. And for that very reason, what a grand feather in the cap of our race to have arranged somehow to keep the poor pulpy animal in an inviolate dodo preserve, simply because all the forces of evolution—up to our own coming—had so beautifully spared it, simply because it was such incomparable proof of a kind of natural selection without tooth and claw.

A craving for the impossible gratification of seeing, touching or hefting the sheltered, innocent bulk of a dodo comes over me strongly in my more whimsied moments. I suspect it must come over every man with any time to think. I believe our descendants will have more time of that kind. I know they will have a lot more dodos than we have, to yearn to have been allowed to see.

Madagascar— a World Apart

More than 200 miles off the east coast of Africa lies Madagascar, an island with a unique and highly diversified fauna. Many of the animals here have risen from stock that came by wind, sea or wing power from Africa and even Asia, and represent primitive and relict forms. But now the forests in which numbers of them have lived successfully for thousands of years are being burned down, and several species are being driven to the brink of extinction.

159

WHEN DISTURBED, THESE SMALL SAP-SUCKING BUGS, KNOWN AS FLATIDS, FALL AWAY LIKE ROSE PETALS FROM BRANCHES. THEY CONSTITUTE

THE ORANGE FROG dwells in damp Malagasy forests. Because its color fades in alcohol, early naturalists were hard put to convince colleagues of the brilliance of living specimens.

An Abundance of Little Things

What it lacks in fresh-water fishes and large mammals, Madagascar more than makes up for in certain kinds of reptiles, insects and birds, all of which were able to bridge the sea gap between Africa and the island. Once established on Madagascar, they took full advantage of its isolation and the lack of severe competition to speciate widely, filling a variety of niches, especially in the thick rain forests along the eastern coast. There are 12 genera of gecko lizards on Madagascar, for example; only one less genus than in the entire Western Hemisphere, which is 68 times larger.

The insect fauna of Madagascar is incredibly rich and incredibly poorly investigated. As might be expected, it has a clear resemblance to the insects of the African mainland but has developed a strong

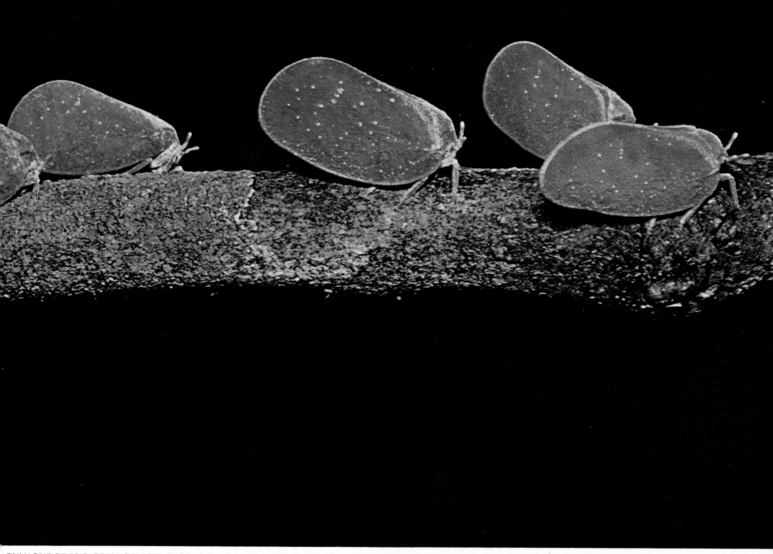

ONLY ONE OF 69 CLOSELY RELATED SPECIES THAT ARE FOUND LIVING ON MADAGASCAR TODAY, AND OUT OF THE 69, 64 ARE UNIQUE TO THAT ISLAND

island individuality of its own. This is most pronounced among such types as the grasshoppers, the cockroaches and some of the beetles. None of these are good fliers, and as a result they have had a better chance to evolve in isolation than strong-flying insects like the butterflies, which are occasionally blown across from the mainland and establish new races in competition with the butterflies that are already there.

One of the mysteries of the Malagasy fauna is how the amphibians managed to get to the island, since they do not take at all well to salt water. One hundred and fifty species live there today and show remarkable diversity. The orange tree frog at left is but one of seven closely related species, all beautifully marked with red, black, yellow, gray or green.

THE DAY GECKO, probably the most spectacular of the Malagasy geckos, is bright green, splashed with red and often blue. It is diurnal in habit, whereas most other geckos are nocturnal.

The Tenrecs

The tenrecs are one of the most puzzling families of small mammals on earth. Almost nothing is known of their ancestry. Logic suggests that they drifted to Madagascar from Africa about 70 million years ago, but only a few tenrec fossils have been found there—and none anywhere else. Today living tenrecs are known only in Madagascar, where, in the absence of competition from other insectivores, they have spread widely into niches that otherwise would have been filled by moles, shrews, hedgehogs and others. There are now web-footed aquatic tenrecs, tree-climbing tenrecs, quilled tenrecs and one species that has probably the longest tail for its size of any known mammal. Altogether there are some 30 species—a few of which may now be extinct—divided into two groups: those that are spiny and tailless, and those with long tails and fur.

STIFF SPINES cover the body of *Setifer*, one of Madagascar's most widely distributed tenrecs. Omnivorous in its diet, it has taken to raiding garbage cans around the capital city.

UP A TREE, *Echinops*, a spiny tenrec found in western and southern Madagascar, clings with sharp nails to a branch. *Echinops* estivates during the dry months in logs and trees.

MOUSELIKE TENRECS of the rain forests sniff among the rocks. They belong to the genus *Microgale*, which includes one of the world's tiniest mammals, a three-and-a-half-inch tenrec.

163

FEEDING, a tiny-toothed tenrec, *Hemicentetes*, maneuvers an earthworm around, preparatory to drawing it in like a strand of spaghetti. Earthworms constitute this species' only food.

THE MOST PROLIFIC OF ALL MAMMALS may be this species of tenrec, *Centetes*. Females often produce litters of 20 to 30 young; one pregnant female was found carrying 32 embryos.

A Useful Echo

Despite the inroads made on their habitats, and the fact that some are eaten by the natives, tenrecs do not seem to be in as great danger of decimation and eventual extinction as the Malagasy lemurs. For one reason, they are less dependent upon the dwindling forests for their well-being. For another, they produce enormous litters. *Centetes (above)* has the highest birth rate of all, and the female is well able to provide for two dozen offspring—she has 24 teats.

As with many evolutionarily ancient animals, the tenrecs are now the subject of extensive research. One scientist, Dr. Edwin Gould of Johns Hopkins University in Baltimore, has paid particular attention to the clicking noises that most, or perhaps even all, species make with their tongues. Gould discovered that these noises are a form of echo location, useful when an animal is exploring unfamiliar places.

But what purpose the sound-producing spines on the back of the highly specialized *Hemicentetes* (*opposite*) serve, no one has yet determined. They may enable individuals to communicate with each other. *Hemicentetes* hunts at night in bands up to 22 strong, including several generations of the same family. According to the natives, as soon as one member finds a worm, it dances excitedly and vibrates its spines, and the others all rush forward, searching the area around it for additional worms.

POSTURING, *Hemicentetes* brings forward its neck quills in a bristling ruff. The most social of the tenrecs, it sleeps in the same burrow with two to 22 others, all often its own relatives.

A NOISEMAKER consisting of 15 spines on the back of *Hemicentetes* has no known function. When this species is excited, the spines vibrate against each other and produce sounds that are, in part, too high for human ears to hear. Similar spines found on *Centetes* young soon disappear, but the area where they grow still vibrates when the adults become excited.

EXTINCT ANIMALS from Madagascar and neighboring islands fill this painting, dramatically illustrating the hazards that beset specialized—and very often vulnerable—insular species. All, with the exception of the elephant bird, the pygmy hippopotamus and the giant lemur, died out after the first Europeans landed on the islands. Dominating the left-hand side of the painting is the flightless elephant bird, which filled a niche that large herbivores might have occupied on Mada- gascar. Directly behind it stands the pygmy hippopotamus, the largest mammal known to have reached Madagascar and a casualty in the Pleistocene. The bird on the branch above the elephant bird is the crested starling of Réunion; it died out around 1840. The bird on the lower branch is the Madagascan coua, which disappeared in the 1930s. In the left foreground is the rail of Mauritius, another flightless bird, extinct for more than 300 years. A giant tortoise, once found on the

Seychelles, is shown facing the dodo of Mauritius, still another flightless bird which was obliterated in the 17th Century. The white dodo behind it, an inhabitant of Réunion, died out a century later. On the right-hand side of the painting, a giant Madagascar lemur climbs a thick vine; it stood almost five feet high. On a low branch behind the lemur sits the broadbill parrot of Mauritius, depicted imaginatively since all that remains to indicate that such a bird existed are two mandibles. On the branch above the lemur perches another inhabitant of Mauritius, the blue pigeon, last sighted in 1830. On a vine to the right is the ring-necked parakeet of Rodriguez, not seen since 1875. Clinging to another vine in the foreground is the uniquely colored parrot of Réunion, known from two specimens and from a painting showing the last of the species, a pet that lived in the King of Bavaria's gardens in 1834. In the corner stands the solitaire of Rodriguez, a relative of the dodo.

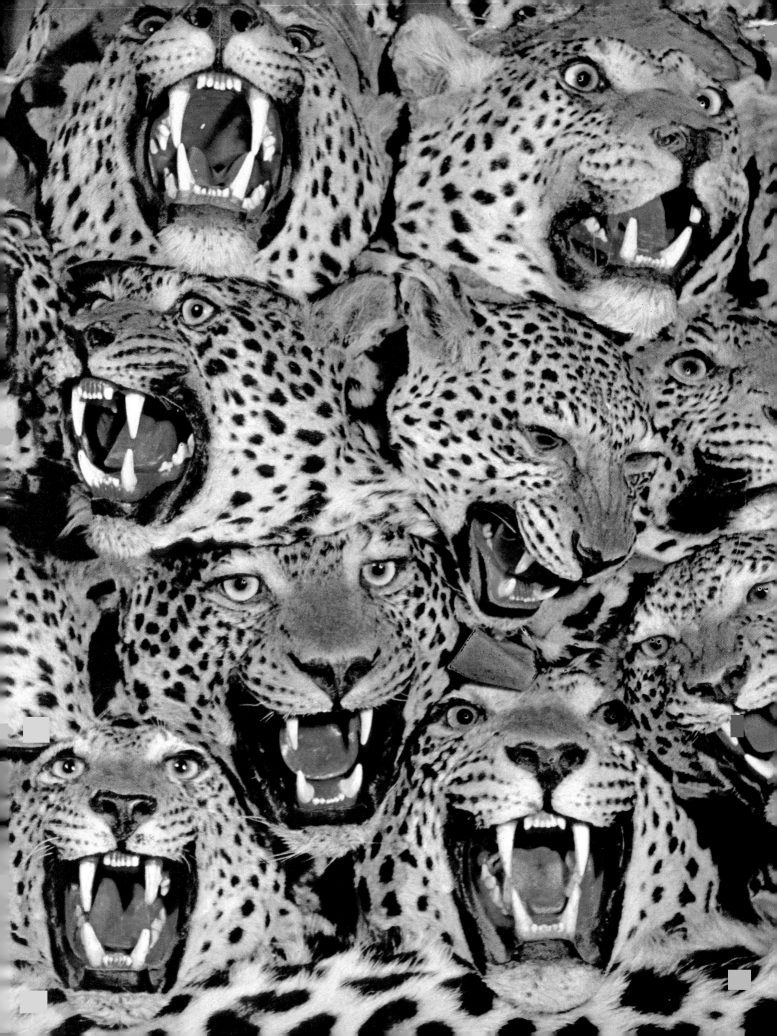

8

Wilderness for the Future

THE world faces a staggering loss in the waning of wild Africa, and concern over the prospect of the loss has finally begun to grow. It is growing so fast, in fact, and in so many quarters, that some people are mistaking the concern for victory. I heard an otherwise sensible man say not long ago that African wildlife is coming back, that there are more elephants in Africa than ever before. This is fantastic and dangerous overoptimism. The animals of Africa, the most splendid array of vertebrate life since the Pleistocene, are not in any state of resurgence, despite the mounting attention to their plight. There may be more elephants in Tsavo than there used to be, and more hippos, perhaps, in the Kazinga Channel and the Victoria Nile. But where are the great herds of animals that once roamed the spaces between the tiny specks of hope that such protected places are?

There is little ground for optimism over the future of African wildlife. There is only a need for realism and for world cooperation in a stubborn fight to save some magnificent small remnants, against odds that appear to be almost impossibly heavy.

In September 1963 the International Union for the Conservation of Nature held its General Assembly in Nairobi. This was probably the greatest rally of world conservation forces that has ever taken place. In several ways it was a heartening success. Individuals and organizations concerned with the situation were made known to each other. In the technical sessions the many-faced character of the problems involved was revealed. New grounds for justifying preservation practice for economic reasons were explored. The governments of the East African countries were impressed by the show of world interest and clearly took away a new understanding of what wildlife can mean to their economies in terms of revenue from tourism, and perhaps from the cropping of game. The proclamation of Prime Minister Jomo Kenyatta of Kenya, published during the period of the Assembly, was a gratifying climax for the meetings. If things go well, as they might, that paper and the Manifesto of President Nyerere of Tanzania, published at Arusha two years before, may one day be seen as key documents in the history of man's tardy flood of conscience over the destruction of the last great fragment of the Age of Mammals.

BUT the Nairobi conference was not the end of the danger. As it drew to a close, one got the feeling that the worst problems had been left for another time that might be too late. I talked with one after another of the people closest to the trouble, and while all seemed glad over the show of accordant concern, none seemed confident that the beginning had been made in time.

The devastation of Africa as a systematic process began with the 19th Century. It began more or less simultaneously in the northernmost and southernmost ends of the continent, with colonization by the French and English in the north, and with the treks of the Boers heading up from the Cape of Good Hope in the south.

In both places the fauna was almost entirely eliminated. When the French colonized Algeria, both antelopes and carnivores were widespread and abundant in North Africa. Lions, especially, thrived from time immemorial, provided with a supplement to their natural diet by the flocks and herds of the Arabs and Berbers. Lion hunting quickly came into great vogue with the white conquerors and, at first for food but later for sport, attention was also turned to the hoofed game of the desert: addax, oryx, bubal hartebeest and dama gazelle. Other North African game animals extirpated over vast areas or nearly brought to extinction were the cheetah, the leopard, the red deer and the mountain-dwelling Barbary sheep. Lions were eliminated from Algeria and Tunisia during the 1890s. The last of all North African lions were killed 10 or 15 years later in Morocco, where Europeans came a little more slowly. The last oryx in North Africa is believed to have been shot in 1906. All this destruction occurred in regions in which the land was mostly waste, where the animals competed for nothing men wanted. Some of the latest extermination has been done with machine guns, it is said, by sheiks who seem to take pleasure in chasing the game in jeeps or Cadillacs.

In South Africa the killing was even more imposing, because the fauna was more splendid to start with. There is no way of making an accurate estimate of the numerical abundance of the savanna fauna of the south. In numbers and in the diversity of kinds of animals represented, it was much like the fauna of East Africa and the Central Plateau savannas. Unfortunately, airplanes did not exist in those days to make the sort of censuses that now are made in the Serengeti and elsewhere in East Africa, so no one will ever know much about primitive population densities in the herds of the Transvaal and the Orange Free State. Certainly the animals teemed there once, and certainly they are gone now.

The destruction that took place here began with the northward treks of the 1830s. The movements of the hardy Boers in their big covered wagons were strangely like those of other people moving westward just a little more slowly in the United States. And the comparison goes beyond covered wagons carrying pioneer families on both continents. Both waves of pioneers moved across land swarming with uncounted millions of hoofed animals. In America the herds consisted mostly of a single species—the bison—with pronghorn, elk and deer at the edges of the plains. In Africa the fauna was the last of the varied grassland community of the Pleistocene. In both places the destruction was almost beyond belief.

As the Boers trekked northward they quickly became wise in the ways of the game, and enthusiastic over the unexpected joys and profits of hunting. They fed their families on game, they sent biltong—the dried meat of antelopes— back to the coast. Hides were used for boots and whips, or were bartered with the natives or sent back to the ports and exported to Europe. And above all, there was ivory. The elephant in primitive times was spread all over the south, in almost every kind of terrain—high veld, low veld, steppe and forest. So with the elephants offering the lure of ivory, with antelopes yielding hides, fresh meat and biltong, with ostriches furnishing black-and-white plumes that set new styles for ceremonial elegance in Europe, the settlers turned themselves into hunters. They fanned out through all the southern part of Africa, and the animals withered away before them.

Before it was over, the land had been remade. The veld, once one of the richest animal landscapes of the earth, had become almost wholly desolate of life. Even the dry fastness of the Kalahari and the Kaffir country was not spared. When the elephants took refuge there, the Boers followed. Within 75 years the fauna was gone from all the open plains and was left clinging to the land only in the concealment of the hills and low-veld bush country. The incredible onslaught was over. The South Africans turned back to their farms, and to their mines of gold and diamonds.

TWO VANISHING PLANTS

South African plants, as well as animals, have felt the ravages of man. Shown here are two with restricted dry-country ranges. Both take a century to reach full size, growing so slowly that they cannot properly replace themselves if damaged by man. Both are now protected by the Government. The one above (Welwitschia mirabilis) has a thick root-trunk, only a few inches of which project above the ground. From this grow a few long, wrinkled leaves. Below is the elephant's-foot plant, a tuber whose starch-filled bulb grows above the ground, protected by thick, corky plates.

IT was out of this dismal destruction that one of the first of Africa's wildlife preserves, the Sabi Reserve, was born. This became the now-famous Kruger National Park and was the prototype of most of the parks that have been established throughout the continent.

The great herds of plains game held on several decades longer in Central and in East Africa, where the magnificent landscapes of the lake country and Masai lands of Kenya and Tanganyika kept their primitive look until the beginning of the 20th Century. Although Arabs from Zanzibar had been exploiting a trade in ivory for centuries, it was not until after 1900 that a new breed of hunter arrived, the professional European elephant hunter. The herds quickly began to be harried by growing numbers of them—Boers from the south, Frenchmen and Belgians who followed Bragga and Stanley up the Congo, Englishmen who swarmed into Kenya and Uganda, and Germans moving west from Mombassa to settle Tanganyika. Elephants were always the prize game. Hippos were killed along the rivers that served as the highways into the land. Ostriches were hunted for plumes, and rhinos for their nose horns, which sold readily to wealthy Chinese who to this day believe in a potion of rhino horn shaved into wine as a prop for waning sexual vigor.

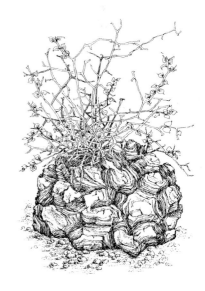

From the beginning the growing posts of colonization were fed mainly by hunters, and guns soon began to fall into the hands of Africans who for ages in the past had had only spears and arrows for killing, and only their own bellies to fill with meat.

With the spread of new people through the lake country and high plains, even the teeming antelope herds began to diminish. Whereas the elephant, hippopotamus and rhinoceros were killed out individually by hunters, the elimination of the plains game came mostly through man-made changes in the lean lands of high Africa. Massive disruptions were carried out in efforts to control the tsetse fly. The ill-fated groundnut scheme, a huge peanut-growing project which was to have brought prosperity to Tanganyika, brought only wrecked landscapes. In the decade after the Second World War it seemed unlikely that any of the original wildlife resource could be saved anywhere outside a few reserves, and possibly not even there.

Now, if the prospect still seems dim, it is not for lack of interest in the problems. It is simply the vast complexity of straightening out motives, the unlikelihood of weathering drastic political change, and the difficulty of learning to manage landscape for the good of present and distant generations that appalls the conservationist.

WEAPONS
WITHOUT HUNTERS

Probably the most deadly weapons employed against African game are the various snares, nets and other devices that are set out in increasing numbers by tribesmen. They are all illegal, and all are cruel. Many of the animals caught in snares die slowly from gangrene or thirst. If they are lucky they will be killed and eaten by carnivores, or else strangle themselves by their own struggles.

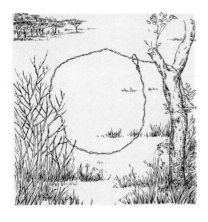

The simplest snare is this wire noose firmly anchored to a tree and stretched across any open space through which a grazing animal can be expected to wander. Antelopes are caught by their necks and quickly strangle, but elephants have been known to have their trunks cut clear through in their struggles to get away.

THE process of saving wilderness has two nominally separate aspects: prevention of the extinction of species and maintenance of wild landscapes. To some extent the two are the same thing. Obviously, if the whole living place of an animal is kept intact, the animal will automatically be preserved. Conversely, the degradation of a habitat endangers the survival of all its occupants, with the jeopardy proportional to the degree of specialization of the species involved. A species with a restricted, specialized habitat will be affected more readily by changes in a landscape than the more ecologically flexible creatures in it. When a highly specialized species has a limited geographic range as well, then destruction of the habitat and extinction of the species go hand in hand. This sometimes does not even need the help of man. Where the range is extremely limited, internal factors may cause such drastic fluctuations as to endanger the species' chances for survival. To guard against such internally generated disasters, the only hope is to provide enough geographic range to take up the shock. Any species being held in one small sample of landscape has a dubious future, no matter how carefully the landscape is guarded.

There are three things that can be done to preserve the remnants of a threatened species. It can be rigidly protected within tracts of natural habitat which are also protected, as in the case of the whooping crane on the Aransas reservation in Texas. It can be kept in a pen, as the last passenger pigeon was kept long after all the other survivors of her once teeming fellows had died. Or it can be introduced to other areas of suitable habitat, in nearby or in distant places, in the hope that it will take root there and spread. This process has begun in the case of the white rhinoceros, now being re-established in parts of its old African range from which it had previously been eliminated. Long ago South African ranchers began protecting individual species of antelope, both to help save the species and as experiments in game farming. Eland have been kept as domesticated stock in Southern Rhodesia for several years, and in the Ukraine for more than half a century. Even such ecologically specialized species as the semiaquatic red lechwe have been suggested as useful subjects for husbandry projects. With any species that can be translocated, grown and marketed for profit, survival is really no problem.

But the saving of wild beings from obliteration cannot be expected to pay for itself in more than a sprinkling of special cases. For most of the wild things on earth, the future must depend upon the conscience of mankind. In its most rewarding and durable form, species preservation is not separable from landscape preservation. Saving of original landscapes is one of the urgent and grievously difficult problems of these complicated times. There are three clearly separate aspects of this problem: to strike a reasonable balance between the need for preserving an esthetic resource and the day-to-day needs of the human population; to prevent poaching in protected or managed areas; and to maintain the organization of the wild ecosystems, once all extraneous factors have been brought under control. Of these the second, though the most violent, is by far the easiest to control. In parts of the game country, poaching is probably already decreasing. Nevertheless it is still a major factor in the outlook for saving African wildlife in a natural environment. Some tribes are easily persuaded to stop poaching. Others, like the Turkana in northern Kenya, are very refractory. Illegal killing of game is done with firearms, now spreading through the backlands in growing numbers, with poison arrows or with various kinds of traps and snares, particularly with noose snares of steel wire or cable. The killing is carried out either surreptitiously or on mob hunts by whole villages. Although the aim is often meat to be eaten or sold, there is a good market for other products of poaching—ivory, leopard skins, rhinoceros horns, and trophies, souvenirs and curios of various kinds. Although such depredations are a severe problem, they are at least an open, understandable one with a known enemy, and with fairly clear paths toward his control.

Far more vexing are the nonviolent inroads of man, the inevitable competition of growing human populations with wildlife for the remaining tracts of wilderness. In true sanctuaries the animals have the land to themselves; no people are allowed to live there. In various other types of controlled areas and reserves, however, the two must live together. Through all the remaining wild areas—neither settled as yet by humans nor designated as sanctuaries—the welfare of the wildlife will have to be reckoned against the rights of multiplying African man.

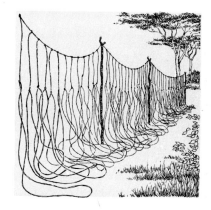

A series of nooses suspended from trees or poles sometimes runs for 200 yards through tall grass where it cannot be seen. Beaters then round up herds of animals and drive them into the nooses, where many become entangled and are easily killed with clubs and spears. These nooses can be made either of rope or wire.

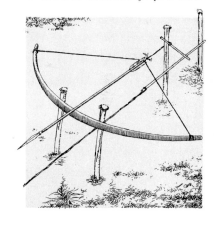

A poisoned arrow is fired by an animal walking into a trip line. The line is fastened to a stick held against two stakes by another short stick which, in turn, is attached by a string to the drawn bow. When the lower stick is knocked loose by the animal kicking the cord stretched across the path, the arrow is released.

An example of the cruel dilemma this mixing of people and wilderness poses is the case of Treetops Hotel, the famous game-viewing station, where elephant, rhinoceros, buffalo and many other animals can be seen and photographed from the comfort of raised viewing balconies. Treetops is in the Aberdare Forest of Kenya, and although situated within the Aberdare National Park, it is only a mile away from a new Kikuyu settlement area recently turned over to Africans for small-farm development. The animals are attracted to the Treetops area by artificial water holes and salt deposits. As long as the surrounding land remained in the big holdings of the European settlers, there was little trouble between people and animals. Now, however, this land is being cut up into small African-owned parcels, and the buffaloes and elephants are wreaking havoc in the gardens. The people are retaliating with guns, and the whole existence of Treetops is threatened. If the animals should stop coming, the effect on the national economy, from lost tourist revenue, would far outweigh any gain that unmolested farm gardens would bring. But this calculation is no comfort to the farmers and they keep on shooting the animals in their sweet potato patches. The only practical solution seems to be to deepen and lengthen a game ditch that separates Treetops from the farmlands. The cost would be heavy, the money is not available, and the Government is now wrestling with its soul over the question of financing the project.

173

Up to the present time, two factors, more than any others, have retarded the ruin of the savanna landscape of East Africa. One of these is drought, which makes much of the land unfit for anything but pastoralism. The other is the tsetse fly, which carries the protozoan that causes trypanosomiasis in cattle and sleeping sickness in man. Much of the tsetse country is good game country, and because the wild animals are immune to the sickness that the flies carry to domestic cattle, they find a partial and temporary asylum wherever the fly abounds. For instance, the world owes the superb Murchison Falls National Park in Uganda to the tsetse fly. Murchison is not submarginal semidesert, but a great tract of fertile land that once was thickly populated. During the 1890s sleeping sickness began to spread through the area, and it was evacuated by the colonial government and later on proclaimed a national park. Without the dread memory of the sickness, it would never have been possible to keep settlers from going back into the land.

In the tsetse-free grasslands, the game herds have lived with cattle-tending Africans for centuries. Until now they have been better adapted to the lean landscape than the men and the cattle, and friction has been negligible. Now, however, preventive medicine and improved nutrition are saving both men and cattle in numbers never known before, and each year that passes, the situation in the common habitat becomes less favorable for the game.

Most of the factors in the relationship between wildlife and pastoralism converge in the case of the Masai of Kenya and Tanganyika. Like pastoralists everywhere, the Masai do not hunt for food; not even their cattle are used for meat except on ceremonial occasions. The main food of the young men is blood and milk; that of the old people is fruit and milk. So in Masai country, poaching is not a major problem. On the other hand, because cattle are a mark of an owner's status, which is measured by the size rather than the quality of his herd, the cattle are not culled or sent to market, and normal checks on the herds are lacking. Because water is scarce and carnivores are about, the cattle are kept in concentrated herds, and the combined close grazing and trampling wrecks both the grass and the water holes. As medical service is extended to the Masai, and veterinary service to the cows, both survive at unprecedented rates and degradation of the grasslands is compounded. The Masai problem is, if not typical, at least symbolic of the enigma posed in Africa. The Masai are no knavish outlaws, perversely destroying wildlife or killing it for illicit profit. Their offense is only a stubborn conservatism that keeps them out in the wilderness, living in the old ways but surviving at the new rates penicillin allows, and so growing into a problem with no solution in sight.

I n Kenya, where the acquisition of land for inviolate wilderness areas is becoming increasingly difficult, the need to adapt rural people and wildlife to each other has been recognized in a special category of land use known as County Council Game Reserves. In these, both human affairs—mainly those of the cattle-tending tribes—and the wildlife are carefully managed, and the revenue from tourism goes to the local district. One of five such areas is the magnificent Masai Amboseli Game Reserve at the foot of Mount Kilimanjaro, which on clear days rises snowcapped as a stunning backdrop for browsing giraffes or mixed herds of antelope. A little while ago the best parts of Amboseli, around the watered areas, were almost ruined by the Masai cattle. Then the County Council deviated water from the park proper for the use of cattle and excluded them completely from the central game area. Recovery of the vegetation cover began at once. It is now deteriorating again under a new onslaught of cattle. The local Masai herders have been exerting heavy political pressure on the County Council, and the borders of the reserve have been breached. What is left is being ruined by tourists. There were 13,240 of them in the Park in 1962. Their cars churned the light volcanic soil into powder over much of the good part of the reserve. Because of the lightness of the soil, no permanent automobile trails can be established, and the cars of the visitors go roaming at will across the steppe. The animals have become reconciled to their intrusion, but the vegetation is being stripped from the lean ground and the soil goes billowing away with each strong wind.

So even if Amboseli can be saved from the cattle, it will be even more gravely menaced by rapt safarists who come from far and near to see its wonders. This paradoxical tragedy, which ultimately has no solution at all except in the control of human breeding, is well known to those responsible for preserving the national parks of America. In the case of Amboseli, permanent roads, ballasted and paved, would stave off the trouble for a time; but the money to build the roads is nowhere at hand.

Another crucial test of will and ingenuity in managing mixed wilderness and people is going on in the Ngorongoro Conservation Area in Tanganyika. Once a part of the great Serengeti sanctuary, this 2,510-square-mile territory has been split off from Serengeti to be made a controlled land-use area, in which forests, water resources, wildlife and the activities of pastoral and gardening peoples are all under experimental management. The center of the area is the incomparable Ngorongoro Crater, an immense flat-floored, extinct volcano about 12 miles across. The floor of the crater lies at about 6,000 feet, and the steep rim around it is about 2,000 feet higher, with some peaks in the nearby highlands going up to more than 10,000 feet.

Within the stunning geometry of its bowl, Ngorongoro has one of the most spectacular displays of savanna wildlife left in Africa. In this vast amphitheater, the whole spectrum of the Serengeti fauna is spread on a short-grass plain with scattered *Acacia* forest and a salt lake set about with waterfowl—all enclosed within the soaring blue wall of the crater rim. Viewed either from below, out on the plain or from the rim looking down into it, Ngorongoro is so dramatic it seems unreal.

Although more nearly a microcosm—a cut-off, self-sufficient unit—than most wilderness reserves, Ngorongoro is not wholly self-contained. Trails slashing slantwise across the face of the rim walls show where the animals go and come between the outside and their little world of the crater floor. The rhinoceros population varies from six or eight to as many as 40 in a single year. The wildebeest herds range in number between 7,000 and 10,000. Most of the larger predators, lions, leopards, cheetahs and wild dogs, are not permanent residents. But at any time of the year, one can see in this awesome place the savanna landscape of high Africa at its most spectacular.

Even Ngorongoro is under trial. In this clearly bounded, seemingly preservable and precious bit of earth, survival is not assured. The trouble is, basically, that there are people in the crater. The people are Masai. Like all Masai, they are well behaved and incredibly colorful and appropriate looking; but their presence complicates the job of keeping Ngorongoro heading toward a stable future as a wilderness reserve. Their sin is simply that they are surviving as they never survived in the old days when their whole lives came from the land.

In their present numbers, with their current customs, they are not a critical threat to Ngorongoro. In fact, they look wonderful there, and some of their pastoral practices actually help hold the land in the best condition for wildlife. But, although the conservative Masai hold aloof from most of the blandishments of civilization, there is one blandishment they cannot be expected to forgo, even to keep Ngorongoro wild. That is the improved life expectancy that medical and veterinary science offers. That is of course the dilemma of man vis-à-vis nature nearly everywhere. In this crater, men could have a treasure forever, and someday the descendants of these same surviving Masai will look back and long to see some small sample of how the world was, and will feel the same keen hurt felt by every reflective man when no sample is left to see. But even the hidebound ways of the Masai do not include any reverence for the higher mortality rates of their forebears. So, like men everywhere, they will go on increasing in numbers never known and finally displace the wilderness that once they clung to.

THAT is the agonizing problem in Africa, to balance the needs of an emerging people against those of a vanishing wilderness. Wherever human welfare is clearly at stake, everything else has to be sacrificed. A prosperous, mellowed society can think of welfare in terms of abstract values, of welfare of distant descendants. To the average African of today, however, those values and that sort of welfare are, and for a time will remain, unknown.

Witness the following letter to a government official from a group of Masai who gave up pastoralism for agriculture 50 years ago and since that time have grown from a few dozen people to 50,000. The man they are complaining about is a neighboring park commissioner.

"Greetings, Sir! With respect we write this letter to inform you of the damage which we have suffered in our farms which have been destroyed by elephants, also with reference to the letter of the Conservator of the 31st May, 1963, which prohibited the Game Scouts from shooting these elephants which are ruining the farms of the people of Endulen. We understand completely that poverty is one of the three enemies of Tanganyika. The people are cultivating in order to get rid of the enemy of poverty, but we people of Endulen are supporting this enemy by following the letter of the Conservator which said that these elephants should not be shot.

"We understand completely that the wildlife which is looked after particularly in this region of Ngorongoro is the property of the whole nation of Tanganyika. The Game Laws state that animals which destroy cultivation must be shot. But the law of the Conservator says that animals destroying cultivation should not be shot: which law should be followed—that of the Conservator or of the Government?

"Your Excellency, this order of the Conservator displays cruelty of a he-goat such as we have never seen in Tanganyika, but only in South Africa where our African brothers are treated thus by the Boers. Further, we say straight out that the Conservator is not here at Ngorongoro to help the Masai, but to hurt them and to keep them down in their previous state.

"This area of Endulen is a place where cultivation was permitted ever since the time of National Parks, and today we citizens are told that we must have a permit to cultivate. Tell me, is this area a part of England? For if someone wants to go to England, he must have a passport. In this area of Ngorongoro it is necessary to have a permit to live!

"Your Excellency, these people whose farms have been destroyed by elephants at Endulen request our honored Government to think why they should not be given the means to get for themselves their necessities. It is as though the people had been caught up in a fire. We await your reply, your Excellency."

So, a great many of the problems of wilderness preservation are made by people—people poaching, people living in with the animals, people coming to marvel at the landscape, to plow it or turn it into real estate. Even where all the problems of people have been worked out, there will still be the unanswered question: can a biological landscape ever be kept intact and wholly natural? The answer seems to be that it cannot. The mere act of setting a boundary to a landscape will bring changes inside. A part of the organization of every natural community is its give-and-take with adjacent communities. Fence off a game area and you may possibly keep the same roster of species for a while, but the balance of their numbers is bound to change, and even their way of life. Migratory animals no longer depart on their customary journeys. They stay behind the fence, and the change in their habits means either fewer of their kind in that place or some compensating readjustment in the ecosystem.

Even conspicuously nomadic species can be restrained in self-supporting enclosures. The elephant is among the most wide-ranging of all land animals in both the habitat of the species and the territory of the individual, and yet there seems some hope that it may successfully be contained in walled-off areas without too-great disruption of the landscape there. In the Cape of Good Hope Province of South Africa, where the spread of settlements and farms makes it impossible to indulge the wandering needs of elephants, about 30 of these animals are being maintained successfully in the little Addo Elephant National Park. The park is surrounded by 11 miles of fence. The elephants make their own living, and they are making it in a bit of their own old territory. Their being saved at all is a wonder, but one may be sure that the biological community of which they are now a part bears very little resemblance to the one that their ancestors lived in.

In maintaining a sanctuary, some of the troubles come from artificially fencing in species, others from fencing them out. Species that are so wide-ranging that they previously entered the tract only sporadically or at certain seasons will now have to be kept out. Some of the larger carnivores, for example, might have to be so excluded, and while no one could predict precisely the effect of this change, no one could expect the community to stay exactly the same. A fenced community will also be cut off from outside sources of animals or plants to replace those lost in catastrophic accidents like epidemic diseases, unusually severe flood or drought, or unseasonable fire.

So, the mere fencing off of a place sets the stage for change. Not only that, any effort in landscape preservation must deal with the even subtler problems of ecological succession. Many of the biological landscapes of the world are what ecologists call climax communities. This means that they have reached a more-or-less stable composition and organization—an ecological maturity—and, barring change in geology or climate, will be able to hold on in that state for a long time, not a long time in the geological sense, but for centuries, say. There are other kinds of communities, however, that are not in this self-perpetuating climax condition, but are undergoing continuous changes in their make-up. If one had time one would see that they were undergoing a slow evolution toward whatever sort of community might represent the climax for that region. This process of community development, by which simpler organizations of animals, plants and terrain grow into more complex organizations, is what we mean by ecological succession. If a forest is cut down and the site burned clean, the tendency will be for it eventually to go back into forest again, and this process will take place through a sometimes predictable series of stages to a sometimes predictable climax condition.

The processes that bring about succession are not well understood. Some of them are not understood at all. In some places it is not even known whether a certain kind of community represents the climax for that region or one of the stages in succession. This uncertainty is one of the complicating factors in the management and maintenance of the African savanna community. Some ecologists think it is a natural climax; others believe it is merely a successional stage, held in its present condition by man-made fire and other cultural influences. For the effects of fire, the shifting cultivations of indigenous man and the manifold influences of the herds of wild game are all involved in the look of the savanna landscape. All will have to be understood and manipulated if the savanna is to be kept the way it is.

This poses a choice for the conservationist. He must decide exactly what it is he wants to preserve. Will he save samples of the various successional stages, halting them in their natural progression toward maturity? Or will he let the landscape go through changes that may leave him with a different community entirely? This may seem to be a somewhat esoteric worry, but in actual practice it is a real one.

D ESPITE all the obstacles and complexities, the fight to save Africa is growing. Powerful support has developed in Europe and in America, and a beginning has been made in the mobilizing of both money and technology. The life histories of African animals are being studied by zoologists, and intensive testing of management practices is under way. A heartening interest has been shown by the new African governments, and effective programs of conservation education for the African citizen are being organized. To some Africans it seems nonsense to be told to preserve the wilderness from which they are only beginning to emerge. And in any case it seems to them presumptuous to be so exhorted when any white man with about $500 can legally shoot an elephant; when white farmers all over Africa have ruthlessly extirpated the animals from their own lands; and most particularly when the foreigners making the most noise about saving African nature have made the most ruin in their own home countries. But because wildlife brings tourists, and because it makes more meat than cattle do on the same poor range, the sympathy of the Africans will come along. Meanwhile, we can only hope that it will come in time to save a few things here and there.

But for me it is sad that the intangible aspects of wilderness are being so dangerously ignored—or not just ignored, actually deprecated. One hears on every hand, "We can't ask Africans to save game for any starry-eyed esthetic motives. One has got to be realistic, you know."

And to be sure, one has to be. But one has to be foresighted, too, and foresee times when tourism will be disrupted, when new techniques of land use make game husbandry as obsolete as blacksmithing is. One must think a long way beyond the life of any material value for wilderness. Thinking that far ahead, the only worth of wild land is the wonder in it, the splendor of old Africa, the look and feel of an unspoiled bit of the original earth.

AN INQUISITIVE BABOON IN NAIROBI NATIONAL PARK ACCOSTS A TOURIST CAR AND INSPECTS ITS STRANGE, CAMERA-CLICKING OCCUPANTS

Face to Face with Man

It is still possible to see an occasional giraffe or elephant, sometimes an ostrich or two, wandering free on the face of Africa. But
for one to find the great game in anything like the variety and
concentration of the past, it is necessary to visit one of the great
national parks. Even there, drought, poaching, disagreements over
boundaries—all these make the future of the animals precarious.

In the Game Preserves

There are about a dozen major game parks in Africa today. Together they contain more than half of the wild animals in the continent, although they represent less than one hundredth of its area. Management varies from excellent to nonexistent. During the Congo troubles a dedicated European, Dr. Jacques Verschurin, stayed on with his dedicated staff in the Albert National Park and kept it from being overrun by poachers. Kruger Park in South Africa is a model of efficiency. Beautiful Amboseli, lying in the shadow of Mount Kilimanjaro, is teetering on the edge of oblivion because its Masai owners cannot agree to keep cattle out. In Serengeti Park in Tanganyika, a recent warden quit because he could not stop the local police from killing game. However, most parks are increasingly well managed and just beginning to face a new problem: how to cope with the rising tide of animal lovers who may well ruin the preserves in their desire to see the very animals they hope to save.

YIELDING RIGHT OF WAY to a large pride of lions in South Africa's Kruger National Park, carloads of sightseers wait patiently while the big cats amble nonchalantly along the road.

Few of the wild animals in Africa's game preserves have had any cause to fear man, and most seem to regard automobiles as noisy and smelly but essentially harmless fellow creatures.

AN ELEPHANT LIES MORTALLY WOUNDED AFTER BEING STRUCK BY A LOCOMOTIVE. IT DIED SHORTLY THEREAFTER AND WAS CUT UP FOR STEAKS

The Bigger They Are, the Harder to Handle

The very size of some African animals makes preserving them difficult. For example, will an elephant capable of pushing down large trees pay any attention to something as flimsy as a fence—assuming that a local government can find the money to build one hundreds of miles long? Elephants are great wanderers, and when they take it into their heads to go somewhere, they go, sometimes with dire conse-

quences (*above*). The hippo poses another problem. A heavy-footed, heavy-feeding animal, it destroys the vegetation in areas where it is permitted to multiply unchecked, thus making future trouble not only for itself but for many other animals as well. A hippo-cropping program has relieved much of the pressure; it is also alleviating the poaching problem, since would-be poachers are receiving most of the meat.

A DECAPITATED HIPPO is rolled away in Uganda's Queen Elizabeth National Park. It was killed to relieve overcrowding, and the meat given to local natives. Game wardens have killed about 4,000 hippos in this park during the last seven years in an attempt to get the population down to about 8,000 animals, where it now is. In return, hippos have killed about 30 humans.

HANDCUFFED POACHERS LEAVE THEIR CAMP WHILE PARK WARDENS GATHER SKINS AS EVIDENCE. IF CONVICTED, THEY WILL SERVE LONG TERMS

CAPTURED SPEARS used by poachers to kill snared animals are displayed by Myles Turner, Deputy Chief Warden of Tanzania's highlands national park, 4,825-square-mile Serengeti.

The Problem of the Poacher

Poaching, regrettably, is still widespread in almost all of Africa's game parks. This is bad for the obvious reason that it results in the slow and painful deaths of many animals—and among certain rare species it may lead to their extinction. However, for most of the commoner species it is not at present a serious direct menace. Rather, its threat is a subtler one. There can be no healthy future for Africa's parks as long as the Africans themselves do not respect law and do not understand that conservation is good for them in the long run. Historically, they have regarded wild animals as a source of food or as crop-damaging nuisances. But as President Nyerere of Tanzania noted, "Americans and Europeans have the strange urge to see these animals, and we must ensure that they are able to do so." Unfortunately, the idea that animals can attract wealth is still generally too sophisticated. Thus the concept of game parks must be explained and encouraged during these critical years while there is still land for parks, and animals to populate them.

STREWN WITH CARCASSES, a poacher camp is burned to the ground. Warden Turner has incinerated as many as 17 camps in a single day. The meat is given to more law-abiding natives.

LION   WHITE-BEARDED GNU   GRANT'S ZEBRA

THE DECLINE AND FALL OF AN AFRICAN SAVANNA

Man's effect on the ecology of East Africa is depicted in this six-page fold-out painting, which shows the savanna as it was a hundred years ago (*above*) and as it is becoming today (*next pages*). The scene is a typical landscape in what was known as the Southern Reserve near Mount Kilimanjaro. In its former condition it was a balanced community that supported a

THOMSON'S GAZELLE   AFRICAN ELEPHANT   TOPI   IMPALA

wide variety of grazing animals, each of which utilized the vegetation in its own way, moving freely across the land and avoiding overgrazing. Flood or drought may have temporarily reduced its over-all population of grazers and their attendant predators, but it always recovered quickly, and for thousands of years was one of the richest game areas the world has ever known. Occasional grass fires started by lightning (*background*) were a part of this balance, clearing dead grass and posing little hazard to the larger animals. The only people in the area were a few cattle-herding Masai tribesmen who wandered widely themselves, ignoring all animals except lions, which they speared to protect their cows. Tribal warfare not

WATERBUCK   BLACK RHINO   HELMETED GUINEA FOWL   GIRAFFE   OSTRICH   AFRICAN BUFFALO

only kept the population of humans and cattle down but it also tended to keep agricultural peoples out of the plains area entirely. Trouble came to this Eden in the 1890s in the form of rinderpest. The wild ungulates caught it, and enormous numbers of them died. However, they made a good comeback, only to be greeted by the establishment of the Kenya-Uganda railroad, which opened up the country to hunters in droves. When war broke out in 1914 the Reserve was caught between British and German territory; soldiers of both sides slaughtered thousands of antelopes for rations, and, for self-protection, any large dangerous animals they ran across during their maneuvers. For what happened after that, turn the page.

THE RESERVE TODAY stands in barren contrast to its former self. After World War I a large-scale attempt was made to develop agriculture on the plains, and a first step in this was to eliminate all wild animals except those in a game reserve established at Amboseli. The game has never really recovered from this wholesale slaughter, nor will it, for in the meantime the land has been overrun by men and cattle. In 60 years the Masai herds have grown nearly 20-fold. The introduction of veterinary and medical services increased not only the size of the herds but also the number of potential herdsmen. But there are other factors too. In the old days only the Masai elders owned cattle; the younger men were busy fighting and

FOLD OUT: DO NOT TEAR

engaging in ceremonial affairs, and had little time for cows. But after a British-imposed peace among the tribes, military duty was no longer necessary. Many a young man who formerly would have had to wait to buy a wife or raid an enemy tribe for the cows he needed for a dowry is now building up a herd of his own. He will build it as big as he can, for the measure of a Masai is the size of his herd. It is these social and economic factors that, now much more than hunting, have brought about the desolate scene shown above. There is simply too much livestock in Masailand today: an estimated 973,000 cows, 660,000 sheep and 132,000 goats. These animals do not spare the vegetation as the wild herds once did.

They are kept in tight flocks by their masters, eating the land bare as they go, and at the same time cutting it to dust with their hoofs. As a result, the roots of the grasses are killed, the topsoil blows away in the wind, the land becomes increasingly eroded, and alternating cycles of drought and flood swing more and more wildly. There is no place for game in this collapsing landscape. There is not even a place for cattle, and the herdsmen have been looking with increasing envy at the green oasis of Amboseli Reserve itself. Heavy pressure is being put on the local tribal council to permit grazing within the limits of the park. Unless it is resisted, the last remnants of a once-magnificent community of animals will disappear.

DE MAURITANIE
REPUBLIQUE ISLAMIQUE
1F50
GUEPARD

REPUBLIQUE DU NIGER
7F
POSTE
JABIRUS
PROTECTION DE LA FAUNE

MADAGASCAR
RF
POSTES GIROFLE
4F

20F
POSTES
REPUBLIQUE
DE COTE D'IVOIRE

½d
Fireball Lily
SIERRA LEONE

REPUBLIQUE MALGACHE
FAHAFAHANA·TANINDRAZANA·FANDROSOANA
POSTES
1F
CHIONAEMA PAULIANI

100F
POSTE AERIENNE
HELICHRYSUM MECHOWIANUM
REPUBLIQUE du CONGO

Famille Papilionidés
GUINÉE
POSTE AERIENNE
RÉPUBLIQUE DE
100F

CORREIOS
3$00
GUINÉ PORTUGUESA

RÉPUBLIQUE DU SÉNÉGAL
POSTES
45F
Papilio nireus

HIPPOTIGRIS
10F
TAUROTRAGUS ORYX
BELGISCH CONGO BELGE

RÉPUBLIQUE
MALGACHE
FAHAFAHANA·TANINDRAZANA·FANDROSOANA
POSTES
SALAMIS
DUPREI
0F50

ARCHIPEL DES COMORES
40F
RF
POSTES COELACANTHE

CENTRAFRICAINE
RÉPUBLIQUE
COLOTIS EVIPPE
1F

1.25F
PROTEA
REPUBLIQUE
RWANDAISE

REPUBLIQUE GABONAISE
POSTE AERIENNE
200F
MELITTOPHAGUS MULLERI

REPUBLIQUE CENTRAFRICAINE
250F
POSTE AERIENNE
AGAPORNIS PULLARIA PULLARIA
INSEPARABLES A TETE ROUGE

0F40
RF
CÔTE FRANCAISE DES SOMALIS

POSTES
RÉPUBLIQUE
DU CONGO
20F
JABIRU
D'AFRIQUE

LYBIUS
BIDENTATUS
POSTES
50F
ETHIOPIA

REPUBLIQUE CENTRAFRICAINE
POSTE AERIENNE
200F
TURACUS PERSEA
TOURACO

3F
POSTES
RÉPUBLIQUE DE
GUINÉE

REPUBLIQUE du SENEGAL
POSTE AERIENNE
100F
ROLLIER

PARC NATIONAL DU
NIOKOLO-KOBA
20F
POSTES
ELAND de DERBY
RÉPUBLIQUE du SÉNÉGAL

REPUBLIQUE
AUTONOME
du TOGO
5F
POSTES
LE COBE DE BUFFON

POSTES
40F
REPUBLIQUE DE GUINÉE

SIERRA LEONE
2d
Black Eyed Susan

BUBALUS
8F
ROYAUME DU BURUNDI

DE MAURITANIE
REPUBLIQUE ISLAMIQUE
25F
PATAS

REPUBLIQUE du TCHAD
POSTE AERIENNE
200F
COBE MOUCHE DE PARADIS
TCHITREA VIRIDIS

REPUBLIQUE DU MALI
POSTE AERIENNE
200F
PROTECTION DE LA FAUNE

POSTE AERIENNE
200F
OUTARDE
CÔTE FRANCAISE
DES SOMALIS
RF

PARC NATIONAL DU
NIOKOLO-KOBA
15F
POSTES
PHACOCHERE
RÉPUBLIQUE DU SÉNÉGAL

REPOBLIKA MALAGASY
POSTE AERIENNE
250F
PROTECTION DE LA FAUNE
PROPITHECUS VERREAUXI COQUERELI

REPUBLIQUE DE
25F
POSTES
CÔTE D'IVOIRE

REPUBLIQUE DU NIGER
100F
LION
PROTECTION DE LA FAUNE

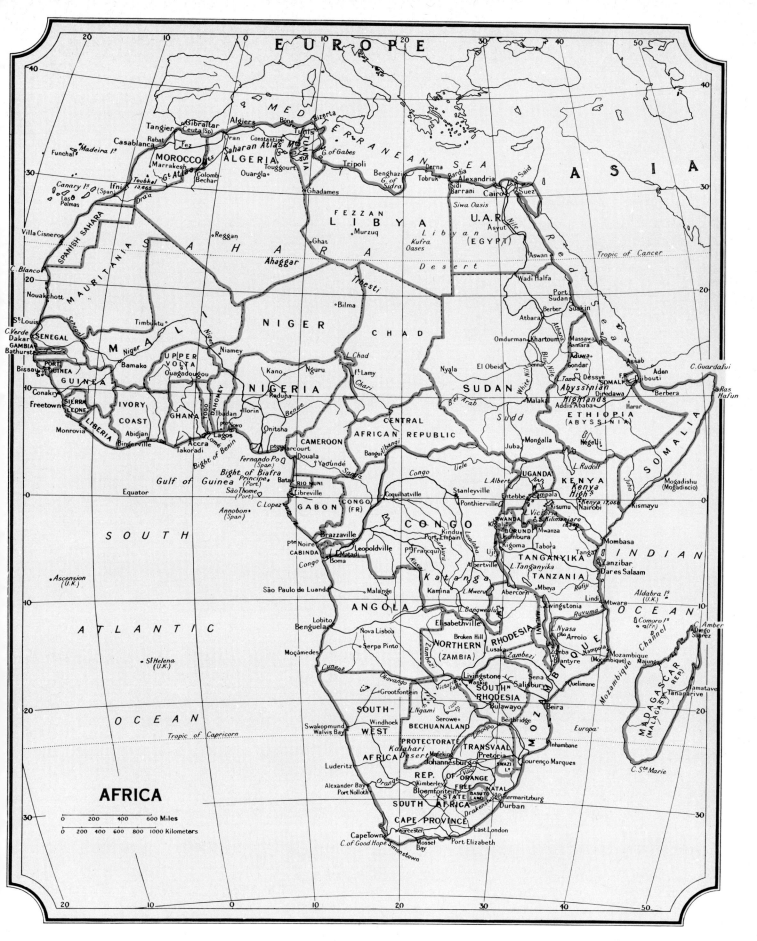

AFRICA

AFRICAN NATIONS PROUDLY DISPLAY THEIR WILDLIFE HERITAGE IN THIS SPLENDOR OF MULTICOLORED STAMPS

Credits

The sources for the illustrations in this book are shown below.

Credits for pictures from left to right are separated by commas, top to bottom by dashes.

Cover—W. Jeffrey Smith from Photo Researchers, Inc.
8, 9—James McAnally from Graphic House
11—Drawings by Otto van Eersel
15—Drawings by Jack J. Kunz
17—Derek Bayes "Copyright Reserved"
18, 19—Anthony Linck—Culver Pictures, Arthur Shay; drawing and map by Adolph E. Brotman
20—Culver Pictures except top right The Bettmann Archive; map by Adolph E. Brotman
21—Culver Pictures, The Bettmann Archive—Thomas D. McAvoy
22, 23—Culver Pictures (2), The Bettmann Archive, courtesy The American Museum of Natural History—map by Adolph E. Brotman, Laurence Lowry from Rapho-Guillumette, Quentin Keynes
24—The Bettmann Archive—Culver Pictures—Eliot Elisofon
25—Emil Schulthess from Black Star—map by Adolph E. Brotman
26, 27—Top center Carl Akeley courtesy The American Museum of Natural History; top right Howard Sochurek—map by Adolph E. Brotman—bottom Robert Halmi
28, 29—Left courtesy The American Museum of Natural History; right Eric Schaal
30, 31—Maps by Lowell Hess
32—Roger Tory Peterson from Photo Researchers, Inc.
34—Drawing by René Martin
35—Drawing by Guy Tudor
36, 37, 38—Drawings by Margaret L. Estey
40, 41—Drawings by Anthony Saris

43—Paul Popper
44—Eliot Elisofon
45—Dmitri Kessel
46, 47—Emil Schulthess from Black Star
48—Terence Spencer
49—Loomis Dean
50, 51—Douglas Faulkner
52, 53—Des Barlett-Armand Denis from Photo Researchers, Inc.—Dale A. Zimmerman, Carlos Stern
54—Bob Campbell-Armand Denis from Photo Researchers, Inc.
55—Terence Spencer
56—Toni Angermayer from Photo Researchers, Inc.
57—William Vandivert
58, 59—Marc and Evelyne Bernheim from Rapho-Guillumette
60—Lee M. Talbot
62, 63—Drawings by Stephen Chan; research by Robert Goetz
64, 65—Drawings by Margaret L. Estey
66, 67—Drawings by Matt Greene
68, 69—Drawings by Jack J. Kunz
71—Emil Schulthess from Black Star
72, 73—Dale A. Zimmerman—Ernst Haas from Magnum
74—Quentin Keynes
75—James Simon from Photo Researchers, Inc. except bottom C. A. Spinage
76, 77—Drawings by Joseph Cellini
78—George Holton from Photo Researchers, Inc., Des Barlett-Armand Denis from Photo Researchers, Inc.—N. Meyers from Free Lance Photographers Guild, Jane Burton from Photo Researchers, Inc.

79—Paul Jensen—Robert Cohen from AGIP, New York Zoological Photo
80, 81—Bernhard Grzimek/Frankfurt am Main—C. A. Spinage from Annan Photo Features, Ylla from Rapho-Guillumette
82—Freddie Yowell, Eliot Elisofon
83—Willard Price—Alouise Boker: National Audubon Society
84, 85—Eliot Elisofon
86—Jean B. Thorpe
89—Drawing by Jack J. Kunz
91—Drawing by René Martin
93—Drawing by Rudolf Freund
95—Dale A. Zimmerman and Marian Zimmerman
96, 97—David Ming-Li Lowe
98, 99—David Goodnow
100—Loomis Dean
101—Ylla from Rapho-Guillumette
102, 103—Willard Price
104—Des Barlett-Armand Denis from Photo Researchers, Inc.—Lee M. Talbot
105—Edward S. Ross—Des Barlett-Armand Denis from Photo Researchers, Inc.
106, 107—Edward S. Ross, Des Barlett-Armand Denis (3)—Edward S. Ross
108—Shelly Grossman
109—Maitland A. Edey
110—Canadian Aero Service Ltd.
112, 113—Drawing by Guy Tudor
115—Drawing by Guy Tudor
116, 117—Drawings by Rudolf Freund
119—Drawings by Chet Reneson
121—U. Rahm I.R.S.C.A.
122—Dmitri Kessel
123—U. Rahm I.R.S.C.A.—Paul Popper
124, 125—Ewing Galloway, Paul Popper

126—Courtesy The American Museum of Natural History, Ewing Galloway
127—U. Rahm I.R.S.C.A.
128 through 133—Edward S. Ross
134—U. Rahm I.R.S.C.A.
137—Drawing by René Martin
138, 139—Drawings by Otto van Eersel
143—Elmar Lindner-Ludwigsburg
144, 145—Dale A. Zimmerman
146—Edward S. Ross
147—Edward S. Ross except center; Elmar Lindner-Ludwigsburg
148, 149—H. von Meiss-Teuffen from PIX, Inc., Edward S. Ross
150—Edward S. Ross
153—Enid Kotschnig
155—Drawing by Jack J. Kunz
156, 157—Drawings by Barbara Wolff
159—Howard E. Uible
160, 161—Edward S. Ross—Robert S. Simmons
162 through 165—Fritz Goro
166, 167—Painting by Guy Tudor
168—Loomis Dean
171—Drawings by Barbara Wolff
172, 173—Drawings by Otto van Eersel
179—Loomis Dean
180, 181—David Ming-Li Lowe—Alfred Eisenstaedt—Ylla from Rapho-Guillumette, SATOUR
182—N. Stipinovich
183—Loomis Dean
184, 185—Loomis Dean
186 through 191—Paintings by Rudolf Freund
192—Courtesy Gimbels Stamp and Coin Department
193—John Bartholomew Ltd.

Acknowledgments

The editors of this book are particularly indebted to Carl T. Gans, Associate Professor of Biology, State University of New York at Buffalo, who read the text in its entirety. They also want to thank the following associates of The American Museum of Natural History: Dean Amadon, Chairman and Lamont Curator of Birds, Department of Ornithology; Sydney Anderson, Associate Curator, Department of Mammalogy; James W. Atz, Associate Curator, Department of Ichthyology; James C. Greenway, Jr., Research Associate, Department of Ornithology; Sidney Horenstein, Scientific Assistant, Department of Fossil Invertebrates; Karl F. Koopman, Assistant Curator, Department of Mammalogy; Malcolm C. McKenna, Assistant Curator, Department of Vertebrate Paleontology; Bobb Schaeffer, Curator, Department of Vertebrate Paleontology; Colin Turnbull, Associate Curator of African Ethnology; Richard G. Van Gelder, Chairman and Associate Curator, Department of Mammalogy; Richard G. Zweifel, Curator, Department of Herpetology; and the Museum's library staff.

The editors also want to thank Herbert G. Baker, Professor of Botany and Director of the Botanical Garden, University of California at Berkeley; François Bourlière, Professor, Faculté de Médecine de Paris; Jon Buettner-Janusch, Associate Professor of Anthropology, Yale University; Glenn W. Burton, Georgia Coastal Plain Experiment Station; Pierre Dansereau, Assistant Director, New York Botanical Garden; Joseph A. Davis, Jr., Curator of Mammals, New York Zoological Park; John Emlen, Professor of Zoology, University of Wisconsin; Robert Goetz, Professor of Surgery, Albert Einstein School of Medicine; Edwin Gould, Assistant Professor, School of Hygiene and Public Health, Johns Hopkins University, and the National Institutes of Health; Harold J. Grant, Jr., Chairman, Department of Insects, Academy of Natural Sciences of Philadelphia; William J. Hart, International Union for Conservation of Nature; Robert Kendall, Duke University; Richard M. Klein, Curator of Plant Physiology, New York Botanical Garden; James Kramer, Department of Entomology, United States National Museum; Björn Kurten, Geological Institute, Helsinki; Daniel A. Livingstone, Associate Professor of Zoology, Duke University; William M. Longhurst, Department of Zoology, University of California at Davis; John Milton, Associate, Conservation Foundation, New York; Fairfield Osborn, President, New York Zoological Society; George Petrides, Professor, Departments of Fisheries and Wildlife and Zoology, Michigan State University; Clayton E. Ray, Associate Curator, Division of Vertebrate Paleontology, United States National Museum; M. A. Sprague, Professor in Soils and Crops, Rutgers University; Carl L. Withner, Associate Professor of Biology, Brooklyn College.

Bibliography

History and Exploration

Day, Donald, ed., *The Hunting and Exploring Adventures of Theodore Roosevelt.* Dial, 1955.

Livingstone, David and Charles, *Narrative of an Expedition to the Zambesi and Its Tributaries.* Harper & Brothers, 1866.

*Moorehead, Alan, *The White Nile.* Harper & Row, 1961. *The Blue Nile.* Harper & Row, 1962.

Richards, Charles, ed., *Some Historic Journeys in East Africa.* Oxford University Press, 1961.

Roosevelt, Theodore, *African Game Trails* (Vols. I and II). Charles Scribner's Sons, 1919.

Sibree, James, *A Naturalist in Madagascar.* Seeley, Service, 1915.

*Simmons, Jack, *Livingstone and Africa.* Macmillan, 1955.

Stanley, Henry M., *Through the Dark Continent* (2 vols.). Harper & Brothers, 1878. *In Darkest Africa.* Charles Scribner's Sons, 1890.

Thomson, Joseph, *Through Masai Land: A Journey of Exploration among the Snowclad Volcanic Mountains and Strange Tribes of Eastern Equatorial Africa.* Sampson Low, Marston, Searle & Rivington, 1885.

General African Wildlife

Akeley, Carl Ethan, *In Brightest Africa.* Doubleday, 1923.

Akeley, Mary L. Jobe, *Congo Eden.* Dodd, Mead, 1950.

Astley-Maberly, C. T., *Animals of South Africa.* Bailey Bros. & Swinfen, 1959. *Animals of East Africa. Animals of Rhodesia.* Howard Timmins, Cape Town, 1960.

Attenborough, David, *Bridge to the Past.* Harper & Row, 1961.

*Cansdale, G. S., *Animals of West Africa* (3rd ed.). Longmans, Green, 1960.

Carr, Archie, *Ulendo: Travels of a Naturalist In and Out of Africa.* Alfred A. Knopf, 1964.

Darling, F. Fraser, *Wild Life in an African Territory.* Oxford University Press, 1960.

Ker, Donald I., *African Adventure.* Stackpole, 1957.

Simon, Noel, *Between the Sunlight and the Thunder.* Houghton Mifflin, 1963.

Sommer, François, *Man and Beast in Africa.* Citadel Press, 1954.

Spinage, C. A., *Animals of East Africa.* Houghton Mifflin, 1963.

Stevenson-Hamilton, J., *Wild Life in South Africa* (4th ed.). Cassell, 1954.

Stokes, C. S., *Sanctuary.* Maskew Miller, 1953.

Ecology

Howell, F. Clark, and François Bourlière, eds., *African Ecology and Human Evolution.* Aldine Publishing, 1963.

Phillips, John, *Agriculture and Ecology in Africa.* Frederick A. Praeger, 1960.

Stamp, L. Dudley, *Africa: A Study in Tropical Development.* John Wiley & Sons, 1953.

Plants

Edwards, D. C., and A. V. Bogdan, *Important Grassland Plants of Kenya.* Sir Isaac Pitman & Sons, 1951.

Lind, E. M., and A. C. Tallantire, *Some Common Flowering Plants of Uganda.* Oxford University Press, 1962.

Palmer, Eve, and Norah Pitman, *Trees of South Africa.* A. A. Balkema, Cape Town, 1961.

†Rattray, J. M., *The Grass Cover of Africa.* FAO Agricultural Studies, No. 49, Food and Agriculture Organization of the United Nations, 1960.

Richards, P. W., *The Tropical Rain Forest.* Cambridge University Press, reprinted 1957.

Riley, Herbert Parkes, *Families of Flowering Plants of Southern Africa.* University of Kentucky Press, 1963.

†Shantz, H. L., and B. L. Turner, *Photographic Documentation of Vegetational Changes in Africa Over a Third of a Century.* College of Agriculture, University of Arizona, 1958.

White, F., *Forest Flora of Northern Rhodesia.* Oxford University Press, 1962.

Insects

†Goetsch, Wilhelm, *The Ants.* University of Michigan Press, 1957.

Harris, W. Victor, *Termites, Their Recognition and Control.* John Wiley & Sons, 1961.

*Richards, O. W., *The Social Insects.* Harper & Brothers, 1961.

Skaife, S. H., *African Insect Life.* Longmans, Green, 1953. *Dwellers in Darkness.* Doubleday, 1961.

Snyder, Thomas Elliott, *Our Enemy the Termite.* Comstock, 1948.

Reptiles, Amphibians and Fishes

Boulenger, G. A., *Les Poissons du Bassin du Congo.* Publication de l'Etat Indépendent du Congo, 1901.

Copley, Hugh, *Common Freshwater Fishes of East Africa.* H. F. & G. Witherby, 1958. *The Game Fishes of Africa.* H. F. & G. Witherby, 1952.

Fitzsimons, V.F.M., *Snakes of Southern Africa.* Macdonald, 1962.

Isemonger, R. M., *Snakes of Africa.* Thomas Nelson and Sons, 1962.

Rose, Walter, *The Reptiles and Amphibians of Southern Africa.* Maskew Miller, Cape Town, 1962.

Birds

†Chapin, James P., *The Birds of the Belgian Congo* (Part I). Bulletin of the American Museum of Natural History, 1932.

Greenway, James C., Jr., *Extinct and Vanishing Birds of the World.* American Committee for International Wild Life Protection, 1958.

Grossman, Mary Louise, and John Hamlet, *Birds of Prey of the World.* Clarkson and Potter, 1964.

Mackworth-Praed, C. W., and C.H.B. Grant, *Birds of Eastern and North Eastern Africa.* Longmans, Green, 1952.

†Rand, A. L., *The Distribution and Habits of Madagascar Birds: Summary of the Field Notes of the Mission Zoologique Franco-Anglo-Americaine à Madagascar.* Bulletin of the American Museum of Natural History, 1936.

Williams, J. G., *A Field Guide to the Birds of East and Central Africa.* Houghton Mifflin, 1964.

Mammals

Ansell, W.F.H., *Mammals of Northern Rhodesia.* Government Printer, Lusaka, Northern Rhodesia, 1960.

Best, Gerald A., ed., *Rowland Ward's Records of Big Game* (11th ed.). Rowland Ward, 1962.

Carrington, Richard, *Elephants: A Short Account of Their Natural History, Evolution and Influence on Mankind.* Basic Books, 1959.

Cowie, Mervyn, *I Walk with Lions.* Macmillan, 1961.

Cronwright-Schreiner, S. C., *The Migratory Springbucks of South Africa.* T. Fisher Unwin, 1925.

Ellerman, J. R., T.C.S. Morrison-Scott and R. W. Hayman, *Southern African Mammals.* British Museum, 1953.

Guggisburg, C.A.W., *Simba.* Chilton, 1961.

Hill, W. C. Osman, *Primates* (Vol. I). The University Press, Edinburgh, 1953.

Schaller, George B., *The Mountain Gorilla.* University of Chicago Press, 1963. *The Year of the Gorilla.* University of Chicago Press, 1964.

Sclater, Philip Lutley, and Oldfield Thomas, *The Book of Antelopes* (4 vols.). R. H. Porter, 1900.

Shortridge, Captain G. C., *The Mammals of South West Africa* (2 vols.). William Heinemann, 1934.

Conservation

Dasmann, Raymond F., *The Last Horizon.* Macmillan, 1963.

Engelhardt, Wolfgang, ed., *Survival of the Free.* G. P. Putnam's Sons, 1962.

Grzimek, Bernhard, *No Room for Wild Animals.* Norton, 1957. With Michael Grzimek, *Serengeti Shall Not Die.* Dutton, 1961.

†Huxley, Julian, *The Conservation of Wild Life and Natural Habitats in Central and East Africa.* UNESCO, 1961.

Robins, Eric, *Africa's Wild Life.* Taplinger, 1963.

L'Union Internationale pour la Conservation de la Nature et de ses Ressources, *Derniers Refuges.* Elsevier, Paris, 1956.

Miscellaneous

Darlington, Philip J., Jr., *Zoogeography: The Geographical Distribution of Animals.* John Wiley & Sons, 1957.

de Beaufort, L. F., *Zoogeography of the Land and Inland Waters.* Sidgwick and Jackson, 1951.

Furon, Raymond, *The Geology of Africa.* Hafner, 1963.

Hollis, A. C., *The Masai.* Clarendon Press, 1905.

Murdock, George Peter, *Africa.* McGraw-Hill, 1959.

†Turnbull, Colin M., *The Forest People.* Doubleday, 1962.

*Also available in paperback edition.

†Only available in paperback edition.

Index

Numerals in italics indicate a photograph or painting of the subject mentioned.